Bellevue Literary Review

*A journal of humanity
and human experience*

Featuring:

*Winners of the 2011
Bellevue Literary Review Prizes*

Volume 11, Number 1, Spring 2011
Department of Medicine
NYU Langone Medical Center
www.BLReview.org

The *Bellevue Literary Review* is published twice a year by the Department of Medicine at NYU Langone Medical Center.

Subscriptions available at www.BLReview.org (1 year: $15 ♦ 3 years: $35)

❧

The *Bellevue Literary Review* was founded in 2000 by publisher Martin J. Blaser and editors Danielle Ofri, Jerome Lowenstein, and Ronna Wineberg.

The Editors of the *Bellevue Literary Review* are deeply grateful to the following people who have assisted with manuscript review: Sarah Bain, Aaron Beckerman, Madeleine Beckman, Amy Bergen, Joshua Bookman, Michael Brabeck, Renata Broderick, Rose Bromberg, Allison Carelli, Susan Cohen, Caitlin Cox, Barbara Daddino, Sayantani DasGupta, Josh Dolezal, Serena Fox, Gloria Francis, Barbara Galletly, Elizabeth Goldman, Bracha Goykadosh, Graham Hillard, Andrea Hines, Emily Hockaday, Ishion Hutchinson, Ed Janowitz, Alison Jarvis, Tyrell Johnson, Aaron Jorgensen-Briggs, Judy Katz, Jackie Keer, Nicole Kouri, Dayle Kramer, April Krassner, Herb Leventer, Susan Malus, Ruth Meehan, Dianna Ng, Scott Oglesby, Ruth Oratz, Patricia Patterson, Lucia Poster, M.A. Rocks, Linda Rogers, Mina Samuels, Smitha Seshadri, Mary Sharkey, Eileen Sutton, Leah Traube, Joe Vallese, Benj Vardigan, Caran Wakefield, Laura Willwerth, and Abigail Winkel.

We are grateful for the help of Lorinda Klein, and for the continued support of Bellevue Hospital.

Cover Note:

Motorized ambulances staffed by Bellevue surgeons, circa 1935-1939

Bellevue Hospital was one of the pioneers of ambulance services. In 1869, Dr. Edward Dalton, the Sanitary Superintendent of New York City, submitted a plan for an ambulance corps based on his experiences in the Civil War. Shortly thereafter, the famous horse-drawn Bellevue ambulances debuted. In 1924, the fleet was fully motorized, and the cover photo was taken roughly ten years later. The Ambulance Surgeons (in white) are standing with their drivers in front of the F&G Pavilion, on the road that would later become the FDR Drive. Many female physicians worked as Ambulance Surgeons.

In 1938 Dr. Morton Galdston, a freshly-minted Bellevue intern, did his month-long rotation in one of these motorized ambulances. He dutifully took notes on the 384 cases he treated. These notes resurfaced when Dr. Galdston retired from a half-century of service to Bellevue and NYU in the Pulmonary Division, and in 1999 he published an account of life on a Bellevue ambulance.* He described the 12-hour shifts with one day off per month, the $15 salary every two weeks, the responsibility for keeping shoes fastidiously polished, and the urgent desire that patients not be DOA—dead on arrival (the penalty for which was buying a round of beer for one's fellow interns).

The catchment area of the Bellevue ambulances included Park Avenue and Gramercy Park mansions, the stench-ridden Abattoir slaughterhouses (site of the current United Nations headquarters), and the Gashouse District slums. The top categories of Dr. Galdston's calls in May of 1938 were alcohol, mental disorders, and injury, followed closely by respiratory and infectious cases. Current Bellevue interns will agree that little has changed. Dr. Galdston passed away in 2003.

* *Journal of Urban Health, 1999:509-32.*

Photo courtesy of Bellevue Hospital Center Archives

Bellevue Literary Review

A journal of humanity and human experience

Contents

Volume 11, Number 1, Spring 2011

Fiction

Nonfiction

Poetry

Foreword

Welcome to the Spring 2011 issue of the *Bellevue Literary Review*. We are pleased to bring you the winners of the annual *BLR* Literary Prizes. We offer our thanks to the Vilcek and Goldenberg families and to the Burns Archive for the opportunity to showcase so many remarkable writers. Of course, we are deeply indebted to our judges and reviewers.

This year's Marica and Jan Vilcek Prize for Poetry was judged by Marie Ponsot. The winner is Janet Tracy Landman, whose poem "Sinkhole" is a delicate meditation on grief. Honorable Mention goes to Cynthia Neely for her poem "Climacteric."

The Burns Archive Prize for Nonfiction was judged by Jerome Groopman. "The Tag," by Elizabeth Crowell, stood out "head and shoulders" for him. The essay is a harrowingly human story of parents facing the birth of a child with a life-threatening illness.

Andre Dubus III was the judge of this year's Goldenberg Prize for Fiction. The winner, "But Now Am Found" by Patti Horvath, is a tender story—equal parts devotion and disillusionment—of a teenage boy in love with a girl who wears a brace for scoliosis.

The Honorable Mention for fiction goes to Jill Caputo. "Winston Speaks" is the vibrant story of Winston—severely disabled, mute—and how he navigates life from his wheelchair and with his aide upon whom he is dependent. When the editors sought to contact Jill about her story, we learned with sadness that she had recently passed away. Disabled by a stroke at the age of 11, Jill became a writer, completing her MFA at Florida State University. She was working at the university when her wheelchair was struck by a car as she crossed a street on August 10, 2010. She was 30 years old.

Much of the writing in the *Bellevue Literary Review* touches upon mortality and vulnerability. Writers often use fiction and poetry— "the great lies that tell the truth"—to mine the emotional depths of these issues. But sometimes the brutal facts of real life jolt us, and can make literature feel rather paltry.

In the waning weeks of August, through September and October, "Winston Speaks" was being passed from hand to hand, as reviewers and editors read, discussed, and debated this story, unaware that the author had been killed just five weeks after submitting it. The story was very much alive for all of us, eddying in our minds as it survived cut after cut of the hundreds of contest submissions. By the time we called to congratulate her, all her listed phone numbers and email addresses were inactive. When we finally pieced together what had happened, and then tracked down her family in Kansas, it felt as though we had lost a close friend.

We had never met Jill Caputo, but we'd experienced an intimate relationship with part of her, absorbed in the intricacies of her narrative voice, living with her story for months. "Winston Speaks" is very much alive, even though the author is not.

It is true that real-life tragedy can make artistic pursuits seem frivolous. There is a certain leap of faith and gulp of guilt that one registers after experiencing illness or adversity, and then reading a poem or writing a story. But literature has always offered succor to patients, families, and caregivers with an intensity that far supersedes the mere scratches of ink on the page. So perhaps it does makes sense, with some curious but compelling emotional logic, to engage literature at these painful moments.

Jill was just beginning her career as a writer, but she was able to use the medium of fiction to convey some of the most eye-opening truths. For those of us who've had the good fortune (some would say random luck) to have not experienced disability, Jill's invented character and made-up story do a more faithful job of communicating the "facts" of disability than most textbooks. It is a gift that extends to the concentric rings of readers who will experience the story, and then pass it along to a friend or colleague or student.

It is with these thoughts that we dedicate this issue of the *Bellevue Literary Review* to Jill Caputo, and offer our thanks to her for graciously sharing her wisdom with us.

Danielle Ofri
Editor-in-Chief

2011 *Bellevue Literary Review* Prizes

Goldenberg Prize for Fiction
Judged by Andre Dubus III

Winner: "But Now Am Found" by Patti Horvath
Honorable Mention: "Winston Speaks" by Jill Caputo

Marica and Jan Vilcek Prize for Poetry
Judged by Marie Ponsot

Winner: "Sinkhole" by Janet Tracy Landman
Honorable Mention: "Climacteric" by Cynthia Neely

Burns Archive Prize for Nonfiction
Judged by Jerome Groopman

Winner: "The Tag" by Elizabeth Crowell

The Tag

Elizabeth Crowell

The bleeding, black letters sprayed on the silver utility box at the corner of Brattle Street and Mt. Auburn Street in Cambridge spelled *Grief.* The G was a hunch-backed giant on which the other, spindly letters leaned. It was a perfect road sign for the place we were going—the Neonatal Intensive Care Unit of Children's Hospital, Boston. Someone heavy with sorrow had waltzed through the dark night to find a place to plant that word. Like all grief, it could only say itself. The event that had caused it was already gone, but its mark in the world seemed to be everywhere.

When we first got the news that the unborn twins I was carrying suffered from a rare and almost always fatal disorder, Cheryl and I saw two birds flying at dusk in a lit, November sky. We took this to mean we would have two babies, not the omen of death it almost certainly was—two blank silhouettes against the cold sky and spidery, desolate trees. The signals from the world were scant and barely recognizable, and we looked for signs everywhere that things might be different than they appeared to be.

Later, in the spring, months after the terrible birth, I saw a dead baby bird, skin shining, beak as hard as bone, part of his mother's egg shell stuck on him, a light aqua, as one might find in an ancient fresco. His eyes were shut. *Don't think it*, I said to myself. *Don't even think it. Neither of your children is this bird. There are no more signs. It is what it is. You have lost a child and your other child is catastrophically ill, beyond anything you ever imagined in any scenario.*

My wife Cheryl and I are good storytellers, the sort people enjoy at parties. And the story of our twins' creation was one we loved to tell. The morning of our wedding—a humid, cloudy August day—I went to get the flowers and Cheryl drove down Rt. 128

to get the sperm. *What a great line, Liz!* After the ceremony and celebrations ended, I got pregnant in our home with twins, two weeks shy of my forty-third birthday.

I'd never met Dr. H—the maternal-fetal specialist performing the eighteen-week fetal survey—but I recognized his reluctant tone. I knew from how he started, with the good news—no genetic defects, two sacs—that there was going to be a "but," and that afterwards there would be a different story.

The twins suffered from twin-to-twin transfusion syndrome, a rare condition only possible with identical twin pregnancies. The shared placenta grows venous routes from twin to twin, instead of just baby to mother. The donor twin transfuses blood to his recipient twin. As the donor dehydrates, the amniotic fluid in his sac decreases to dangerously low levels. The recipient twin suffers from the pressure of the extra blood and so urinates constantly into his forcefully expanded sac. Eventually, his heart is overwhelmed by the fluid pressure. If the recipient twin dies *in utero*, a rush of fluid surges back to the donor twin, almost always resulting in severe brain damage or death.

As we left that day, Dr. H said evenly, "This is not your fault."

"I don't think it is," I replied. It is possible that I am an unreliable narrator in my own story.

Dr. H's earnestness was more apparent the second time we met with him, when we weren't hearing the bad news for the first time. In a full-lit room not dimmed for ultrasounds, he was a handsome, dark-haired man, a decade younger than Cheryl and I.

He told us there were some clinical options, but few. The one that sounded reasonable to us was a procedure called amnio-reduction, in which the doctor inserts a needle into the sac of the recipient twin with the practical goal of reducing the fluid pressure and allowing room for more, inevitable fluid to enter. Then there is the hope—faint but distinct—that this might "recalibrate" the sacs, and reset things to normal.

Cheryl suggested to him that the statistics were very bad—a less than ten percent chance of delivering two living, healthy twins.

Dr. H shrugged and said what ended up being the most helpful thing anyone said to me during the pregnancy and the terrible months that followed: "Those statistics are not your children."

I had to keep reminding myself that we didn't know what was going to happen. This was the human condition in which we lived all the time. We couldn't write ahead in our own story.

We wanted Dr. H to know that we were not parents who wanted these babies to live at every cost to them or to suffer. This was a conversation that we would have more than once, though now I feel it almost as a lament. Of course, everyone would do everything to make sure that we gave the babies their best shot at life without suffering, though suffering is a part of any life, and the quality of suffering in an unborn child or preemie is not really knowable or quantifiable. And we did not want to suffer ourselves. We didn't want our hearts to blacken and die from this. We didn't want to have to make terrible choices.

All parents feel the separation of their young child's life, even for brief periods, as almost unnatural. We do not want to live without our children. We can't even imagine it, and when we do— when we go to that dark place—we feel, innately, that we don't belong there. We do not have as much choice as we must believe. We are not entirely of the world that we walk through, which is darker and more natural than what we want to feel. The children who grew in my stomach in those months, grew in tremendous peril, precariously, with the occasional invasion of a needle as Dr. H managed the sea of fluid, pushing that thin lifeboat through their dark night.

Yet, I continued to teach high school English, as I had for a dozen years. I tried to ignore the children who die in the literature I teach—Macduff's children in *Macbeth*, "all his pretty ones," as he puts it; the twins that are cast into the Evil Forest in Achebe's classic *Things Fall Apart;* and the young man who died for Greta in Joyce's "The Dead." Saturdays, I went to coffee shops to grade papers—teasing out main ideas, coaching sentences into order.

Inside of me, my children fought off their own demise. And there was little I could do. I wanted to go right into that darkness, for I felt as if I were living there anyway. But I wasn't. I was still living in the world, and I would continue to no matter what happened, which was the strangest part of all.

During an appointment in late January, twenty-five weeks into the pregnancy, Dr. H wheeled the chair away from the ultrasound machine, wiped the gel from my belly, and said gently into the darkened room that he thought we would be delivering these twins sooner rather than later. He could take more fluid off, but as of this point we were "risking fetal demise." We had to get them both out before one baby expired, or else the rush of blood from the dead twin would push back and kill the surviving twin. We had to weigh the life of one against the other.

"It's too early," I protested.

"I agree," Dr. H said. We all sat with that for a moment. Then he added quietly, "You asked me to tell you when."

I have a twin brother. We are neither close nor distant. He is a physicist; I am a poet. My parents think it is our essential natures to be so different, though both he and I know we were confounded by our closeness as children, the intimacy of sharing our bodies. We looked a lot alike at a time when twins were still somewhat of a rarity. This was before ultrasound, and the doctor had insisted, despite my mother's pleas, that she was having only one baby.

During the appointments with Dr. H, I could barely look at the white rush of the babies on the monitor, the black lake around one, the tight sac around the other. Yet, I did look at the heartbeats' distinct buttons of movement. The beat of them, amplified by the ultrasound machine, sounded like a rush of horses on a grassy field somewhere.

Finally, Dr. H would measure the umbilical flow, turning up the volume to what sounded like a sonic boom. We were hearing the lush, dark wood we could listen into but never enter. I thought of how silently my brother or I came into the world, in stealth, causing surprise and delight in our family. Two instead of one, both healthy, full-sized, one hiding the other's heart. I tried to imagine what it would be like to know I had had a twin who had died, to whom I had been intimately, lethally connected, who was the person I would not grow up next to, fight with, compete with, and love. How would I experience that loss?

That conversation we had with Dr. H in the dark room was the last time I believed we might really have two, live babies, that I could get more time out of the pregnancy. A day, two days, maybe two weeks, each day a muscle, holding those babies in place. After that, the days crossed and loosened for months until I wished them over.

Dr. H thought it might be best to admit me to the hospital and administer steroids to strengthen the babies' lungs. We made the decision together to wait at least a few days. These babies were about to be our children. Underneath the gathering picture was the *pentimento*, the intention of what we had meant this pregnancy to look like and be. Though the loose, imagined sketch of our family had sunk into the real image, I could still see right through, to what was already gone.

By the window in Pre-Partum, I stared out at the light snow against the dark black of Brookline Avenue. On the lawn of the private school across the street, two wolf decoys were set up, presumably to ward off the geese that came up from the Muddy River and the Fenns. The Muddy River and the Fenns are part of the Emerald Necklace that famed landscape architect Frederick Olmstead designed to hang around the city of Boston. The clustered jewel of these city hospitals is set back from this necklace.

Grief makes bright such particulars. Even as I was moving towards the delivery, or perhaps because I was, I considered the effectiveness of the decoys. They looked threatening, stolid. Would the geese sense danger and turn away? They would be wrong if they did. Perhaps all my instincts about this delivery were wrong. Maybe there was something I didn't see. And wasn't there proof enough—as the geese cluttered the lawn regardless of those lupine ghosts—that the world just is, and the danger is, in fact, inside of us?

After the Caesarean cut, Dr. H coaxed the uterus, pushing down so hard there were inky bruises on my belly for weeks. The sound of the water spilling on the floor stood inside me like a picture. We asked the doctor about his shoes. His shoes? We wondered how he avoided that splash every time. That was what we talked about after our child died.

We had never learned the gender of our babies, despite the dozen ultrasounds we'd had. But, after they were born, they were hustled so quickly to the neonatal teams, that this little fact was lost in the shuffle. I remember having to ask. One of the nurses told me they were boys, and then Dr. H said, "I knew that."

Already, Dr. H seemed farther away and part of the past, as if enough had now happened for there to be a real history. I remember looking up briefly before he did the cut. His hands were in the air, patiently waiting for the sterile fields to be set. He didn't say anything, but I'd found that when he was concentrating, as when he was doing an ultrasound, he tended to focus in quiet. I liked this about him. Yet, at the brink of everything, there was a hush and a fade, and I wished I could take his words, "It's not your fault," from that first visit and place them here.

The neonatologist brought James over to us. His tiny, dark face was wrapped in the bright nursery blanket. We spent an hour with him, Cheryl and I taking turns holding him. Though his heart was still beating, there was nothing that could be done to counter the transfusion damage. Time was slack, and that small difference between living and dead was untraceable. We didn't see it at all in the tiny closed slit of his eyes or feel it with the one finger of our hand that lay on his brief cheek. At some point, his heart stopped. He was so weightless, that when we had to let him go, it was hard to feel the emptiness in my own hands. I don't even remember being reluctant to yield his body.

Matthew weighed one pound, four and six tenths ounces. He had no kidney function. The night after his birth, he suffered a bowel perforation. A pod of surgeons traveled over from Boston's Children's Hospital and drilled draining tubes into his tiny body, hoping that the perforation would seal on its own. By day three his blood pressure had plummeted to dire lows and intense drug therapies weren't working.

And there we were, back at the question of quality of life, of reasonable measures, sitting with doctors and social workers in a conference room with the wintry, gray skyline of Boston behind us. Three days before, we had lost one son, a loss that I couldn't even touch, though it was everywhere. Now we were on the brink of losing the other. And even as he lived, the fluctuations in blood pressure might be damaging the vessels in his brain. Suffering, cost, worth, measures. A pound and a quarter. We agreed to have Matthew be DNR. We would not try to resuscitate him if he expired.

Matthew lay with his eyes covered, on a bed of fleece, naked besides his teeny diaper. We had put up the tiny footprints someone had thought to make after his birth, so light on the powder blue paper, as if what he really meant to do was to step into the world and then step out of it again.

Then, one day, he peed—a tiny, golden fleck in his diaper, the most beautiful thing I had ever seen, a signature of his arrival from the brink of death. For a week or so, he seemed to stabilize. We settled into a routine of going to the NICU, memorizing the menu options in the cafeteria and the food court across the street, debating about the routes in and out, the parking lot levels. And then, he began to slip away again. He had air in his abdomen; the perforation in his bowel had opened. His white blood cell count rose. The posse of surgeons arrived again in the middle of the night.

Here we were, with yet another doctor, discussing the quality of our son's life and whether it was worth it to put him through this, and whether he would even make it. The bowel needed to be resected. The surgeon would pull the intestine outside of his body, where it would sit for several months until healed. Later, he would have another operation to put it back in. There was no way to know how much bowel had been damaged or how much he would lose. He would probably die of sepsis if we didn't do the surgery. Perhaps the perforation would heal on its own, but this was very unlikely. The surgeon said, "I could make up stories as to why he doesn't need this surgery, but he does."

We agreed to the bowel resection and Matthew was taken by ambulance across the street to Children's Hospital that night. Cheryl and I followed on foot; it was dark and cold and the buildings loomed tall and light-dotted above us. *This is your life*, I said to myself. The only way I could reassure myself was to hope that someday this would all be over, and we could just go home and get some sleep. I couldn't imagine taking Matthew with me, taking him anywhere.

But he lived. For reasons no one really understands, except that on some protoplasmic level he was remarkably strong, he tolerated the surgery magnificently, and though there were complications, none of them was life-threatening. Despite the fact that he was critically ill and barely could feed at all, he somehow managed to gain strength, grow very gradually, and endure the hills and valleys of learning to breathe during his three months at Children's.

The first time I held Matthew, he was as light as a necklace. I tried to believe that this was all right, that I wasn't supposed to repel him. Stiff and wooden as those decoys on the lawn, I felt like the ghost of the mother I thought I should be. I felt I might be the most dangerous person to him. His startling, blond hair was warm on his tennis-ball sized skull as he nuzzled against my bare chest. He was not supposed to be born for another two months. He stretched his throat, unable to cry yet, and leaned his fuzzy head against my skin, as if he had just landed from a long, sky-filled journey with no signs, with nothing he could tell me about.

We lost the footprints. They fell off when Matthew made the milestone transition from the isolette to the crib, and were swept away by the cleaning staff, along with all the sticker backs, syringe tops, cloth tape, alcohol swipes, and all the materials that keep small babies alive. We had lost one of the few markers we had of the beginning of his life. Then, I had this dreadful thought. We had James's footprints in the box of things the hospital gave us. James and Matthew would have identical footprints. We could use those. *Use them? For what?*

It's not your fault. I would take those words and try to hold on to them, try to turn the pitch of them to something more convincing. I had lost my child. He was nowhere I could see, though every time I looked at Matthew I thought of how he would look just like that. Cheryl and I shared so much during those months, but she did not have this weight, this guilt that something inside of my body had caused this.

Because the loss of James was so total and also so absent, the sinew of that guilt was everywhere. In an odd sense, it was even reassuring. When I tried to put it to words, or when I looked at the few pictures of James and thought, "you did this," I could hear the irrationality of my thoughts. Yet, as long as I played a part in it, I was held in place. James was not alone in that strange, dark wood into which I was not invited, not even to carve, as the graffiti artist did, a word of absolute lament.

Once, we saw *Grief* again on one of the many back routes Cheryl and I chose to beat the traffic to the hospital. The word stood bigger, brighter, sprayed on an old brick wall that had been the side of a factory, near a convenience store in Belmont. So, grief was someone's tag, a trademark, a signature in the world. For all the places where it went unannounced, this stranger wrote, *Grief* was there. I thought it was brilliant.

I was driving by Fenway Park on the way home from the NICU. It was a sunny day, and zealous fans, donned in red, lined Brookline Avenue, headed towards the game, where they'd eat Fenway Franks and sing "Sweet Caroline." By then, Matthew had had all but his final surgery, and there was clear evidence that not only would he live, but that he appeared not to have suffered long-term damage. His intestine, which had sat outside him like a fat spring worm, was now tucked back into his firm earth. I was thinking we would take him to Fenway Park in a few years and buy him hot dogs. Maybe he would collect baseball cards or play Little League. And James would not be there for that. They would not sit shoulder to shoulder there, elbows touching each other, identical caps on their heads.

Because he was having trouble learning to feed, Matthew needed to return to the hospital where he was born. It was two seasons later; winter had faded to spring, and now summer. I ran into Dr. H. in the halls. I had seen him only once since the birth and hadn't talked to him for almost three months. I told him the good news about how Matthew was doing, and we chatted amiably for a few minutes. It felt very odd, as if I were in some early twentieth-century novel by Thomas Mann or Henry James, where characters who spent some season of love and loss on a boat crossing the ocean or at a sanitarium or a hotel in the Alps run into each again in some other season, after the love or grief had passed. I could barely contemplate what we had shared. It wasn't until I walked away that I could feel myself shaking. I shuddered down the steps to the lobby, where I had to hold onto my legs. He was one of the few people to have held James.

   The day before Matthew went home, I walked around the Longwood Medical Area like it was my college campus the day before graduation. That was the restaurant we were in when we found out he had to have heart surgery. That was where we were eating, when he had to be re-intubated. That was the door we came out of in the middle of the night. That was the parking exit where we'd gone home without either child, after four days in the hospital. The lawn of the private school where I'd seen the wolf decoys in the snow was now lush and green, and we'd watched girls play lacrosse there all spring.

Matthew is two years old. He speaks in full sentences and talks in bargains, "How about ice cream? How about movie? How about watch TV?" He has thick, blond hair and luscious blue eyes. His skin, once so yellowish, is flushed and perfect. He has a good giggle. His whole torso is mapped with scars—heart surgery, three abdominal surgeries, a triple hernia. In the months following those surgeries, occasionally a stitch would float to the surface of the skin from his mysterious, mighty body. Similarly, my own guilt and grief still rises suddenly, a dark strand that can sit over me for days or months. I try to flick it away, to pull the last piece of it out of myself.

After Matthew was born, I wondered how I would ever be able to describe how small he looked. I settled on his ears, which were as thin as paper. Sometimes they would fold over and crease, and the delicate fingers of a nurse had to peel them back. That is something I don't have to put down. It's there with me—the small beauty of a pinkish, luminous ear and its corridor from whence Matthew would eventually startle at the sound of the monitor blurting out its mundane complaints that he breathed too little or too much, where he would learn the sound of our voices, calling his name, where two years later the sound of any music brings him such delight he claps his hands and sings along, as if to prove to me that I have chosen the right sign from all the dark signs of his body that he would stay. ৪০

Sinkhole

Janet Tracy Landman

You would have said you were over it.
It was after all seven years.
And you would have been right
and you would have been wrong
for it seems it was more
than the one thing and
underground the more than one
things had been joining forces
and one day the vibrating earth
started to give way and you lay down
where you were and let it happen.

ಐ

But Now Am Found

Patti Horvath

Metal

The brace encased her, chin to hip, hard plastic and metal. She wore it for her spine, that snaky column, a second body to reshape the damaged one. Winter the metal at her neck was cold, filmy with fingerprints; summer it was too hot for him to touch. She hid it with turtlenecks, smocks, silky scarves. Her shoes big and clunky—*for support*, she said. At movies, at meals, under glass-shaded lamps in the library where they studied, she sat upright, unable to bend. Wispy hair fell into her face whenever she leaned forward. His own hair nearly as long—*Like Jesus.* She said it to tease him, and in retort he called her Teacher's Pet, extending the phrase, hard on the "r." Good girl, ambitious girl, yearbook editor, chorus soprano, player of bright riffs on her parents' secondhand piano. So different from his slacker habits, classes skipped, joints smoked beneath the bleachers at lunch. The activities kept her parents off her back, she said, and she'd knock on her metal torso. It was what he loved about her—the breeziness, her confidence despite it all.

The brace would be until she stopped growing and some extra time to be safe. How long precisely, who could say? Every three months she went for checkups.

He tried to imagine what it was like for her. The weight of the brace lifting from her hips. The paper gown, the x-ray machine, her spine illuminated on the light table. The doctor's finger tracing wayward vertebrae. His veined hands, hairy at the knuckles.

The day he saw the swan he knew he would buy it for her. A silver swan, its chain clipped to the velvet-backed tray in the mall's jewelry cart. One eye in silhouette: tourmaline, beryl, malachite, jade, chemical words recalled from Earth Science class, fancy words for green. There were other things he thought she might like—silver hoops tiny enough not to bang against the brace, a circular broach. But the swan was special, sprung from ugliness, then look! Like the beauty he saw in her, locked away. A month of yard work the necklace cost, four consecutive Saturdays spent raking dead leaves into plastic bags, but what was that? Their anniversary nearly here, a year from the day she'd agreed to meet him at the movies, and it was at the movies that he handed her the wrapped box, waiting until the lights rose and the theater began to fill for the next show.

The way she looked at him, so seriously, mouth turned down as if in disapproval, for a moment he was afraid he'd done wrong. She lifted the swan from its cotton bed, let it dangle between them, its eye a cold green speck. Not real emerald, he explained, but the silver, that's real. She smiled, touched a knuckle to her eye. Was she crying? The theatre was so dim. He wiped his glasses on his shirttail. It's lovely, she said, help me with it.

He had trouble threading the chain beneath the metal at her neck, attaching the clasp. The necklace did not hang quite right, the swan nearly concealed by a crossbar of some sort. But they both knew it was there and that was what mattered, she said.

His second gift, a month later, was almost better, the driver's license they'd been waiting for. With this came a shift in his status, her parents expecting to meet this boy who would take their daughter out, drive her places in his parents' car.

Because he was nervous he smoked a joint on the way over, just a hit to calm him so that later, sitting on one of the matching floral armchairs in her living room, chatting with her mother about the courses he was taking (Algebra I, Intermediate Spanish, Biology, Civics, nothing special, nothing AP, homeroom their one period in common), he hoped the Tic Tacs masked his breath. A white crucifix hung behind the couch, Jesus caked in plastic blood. The only other artwork a painting of an ocean at sunset…or was it sunrise? Wondering this made him want to laugh; he shouldn't have smoked. Her upright piano was against one wall, but not a book in sight; how did she get so smart? Her mother's face a crumpled bag, blond hair gone to rust. She wore an apron, offered sugar cookies and pink lemonade, warnings about speed limits and curfew. The movies, Mom, her daughter groaned. We're only going to the movies.

Her father he saw briefly and just that once. A big squared-off man with meaty hands. When they shook hello, he felt the man's high school ring, a gaudy thing, gumball sized. His grip too hard. If there's trouble, he said, leaving the sentence unfinished. Other times he heard the man banging away in the basement, hammers pounding, drills boring holes.

He thought it would change things, being able to drive, spending time alone with her, but it didn't seem to much. At the movies they still shared tubs of popcorn, scrabbling through kernels until she shushed him, then holding hands through the rest of the show. Always during the week she was busy but sometimes he'd sit with her in the library and pretend to study while she worked. Once he took her to the beach, parking as far as possible from the other cars—couples in back seats, boys doing donuts, their tires screeching on ice. He kept the radio low so it didn't matter what song was sung, the vocals a backdrop to soothe or excite. The heat was cranked high and they took off their coats and sweaters. She loosened his ponytail from its rubber band, smoothed the hair over his collar. He loved how her hair smelled, the sharpness of it, lemon and pine. With her he could imagine himself someone ambitious, an A student, scholarship material, someone to make parents proud.

He reached across the driver's seat, pulled her towards him, awkward in the tight space, her brace making it even more difficult. They had kissed before, of course, in the dark of the movies or briefly before saying goodnight. Not like this though, with his arms around her, the windows fogging and the squeal of tires growing faint. He stroked the coarse wool of her shirt—an arm, a shoulder—inching his way towards her breast, touching instead something foreign—a buckle, a strap—that made him recoil.

I know, she said. It's in the way.

No…it's all right…it's just…

The thing you don't expect, was what he wanted to say. Hardness where softness should be. Metal for flesh, a thing with no give.

Uncertain what to do, he kissed her again, lightly, ignoring what was between them until he forgot it altogether and they nearly missed her curfew.

A Sunday, she told him she'd faked cramps. He biked across town, concerned because it wasn't like her to lie. What with the sermon, the hymns, the jelly donut social, her parents would be gone for hours. Still she'd urged him to hurry.

No one answered the door, so he let himself in. Her shades were drawn, the room dark to hide that she'd been crying. Something about a grandmother. She sobbed, barely coherent. Her grandmother down south, mobs of cousins she barely knew. Floppy-eared, living in shacks. The way she described it—cows to milk, chickens pecking worms. *The middle of freakin' nowhere. All July and August. It isn't fair!*

He would forget about her.

No he would not. She had to believe him.

She stomped her foot. The stupidity of it. And what she did next astonished him, pulling her shirt right over her head, throwing it to the floor.

Look at me! Look! As if things aren't crappy enough.

Ribs, clavicle, shoulder blades, he stared at her fragmented body. Flat breasts in a white cotton bra. Two bars attached to a molded corset, like a pair of metal suspenders. There were screws, bolts, springs, straps. How could she stand it?

She sat on the bed, almost as tall as him because the brace held her rigid. Her eyes red-rimmed, the lids puffed. If he could touch her, reach into that awful cage. Wait, she said. I want you to see. His stomach churned with excitement. She kicked her pants loose and stood up. A greasy leather strap locked the corset in place over white bikinis. Her arms were gooseflesh; what would her stomach look like? He could feel himself growing hard, wanting her.

Take it off, he whispered. Just this once.

I can't. I won't be able to get it back on.

I'll help.

You don't know how. It's tricky.

Show me.

He lifted her hair, loosened a screw at the base of her head. The metal neck ring slid apart. He locked it back in place.

See? What else?

I don't know.

Sssshhh…it'll be easy. You do this all the time.

Not alone.

But you're not alone.

He unbuckled the corset and the brace shifted, loose on her hips. He pried it apart. She did the rest, pushing it from her body, stepping out.

Without the brace's support, she leaned slightly to the right. Porcelain, he thought, meaning not her skin, which was pale from lack of sun, but the bones themselves, how fine they were, how easily he could imagine them shattering. He put his hand on her stomach, the slack muscles beneath making him nearly weak.

From the pocket of his jeans he removed a crumpled joint. Are you crazy, she said; it'll stink up the whole house. He ignored her, raising the shade to blow a long hit out the window then stubbing the joint on the sill. She was sitting on the bed, frowning, but not really angry he could tell. What did she want? He took off his glasses, his shirt. She kept on her underwear and the swan that she always wore. They made a tent, holding each other beneath the covers, hiding from what would come next, her slack-jawed grandmother, the cousins in overalls; they couldn't be as bad as she said. He pressed himself against her, felt her breasts through the thin cotton of her bra, thinking he would be happy enough to die right there until she said we better stop.

The brace would not fit.

He'd managed the leather strap all right but the ring at the back of her head would not come together and when he tried to force it the brace's lower part pivoted, causing her to cry out. Oh shit oh shit oh shit she moaned and he tried taking it apart, starting from the top but the strap would not buckle and her parents would be back any minute, she'd think of something, she said, only he'd better go. He kissed her in a rush and biked fast all the way home.

Afterwards there was silence. Her phone privileges revoked. She's not allowed to talk, her mother said, you'd better stop calling. That stern woman with her apron and sugar, her mouth a jagged line.

He waited in homeroom, at the cafeteria table they shared; he went to the yearbook office, the music room. No one had seen her. At night he would ride past her house, the lights always off and her father's car missing from the driveway.

Fire

The postmark was smudged, the card showing a chapel, white and scabby against a bright sky. And the name, Salvation Valley, printed in red across the bottom.

You are on the forbidden list—can you believe such a thing?—but I found a way to sneak this out. Do not write back. Here they make us rise at dawn, the days being spent in chores and prayer. There are hikes, testimonials, a beat-up piano, out of tune. I tried to warn you. Love.

He fixed on that last word, one they'd never said. How to read it, how to understand. He pictured her scrubbing potatoes, hoeing weeds, hands raw, fingernails dirty and chipped. Always she'd kept them meticulous, the better to play. The piano would be battered, with rough yellow keys, but it was something at least, some small consolation. At prayers she knelt on a splintered floor, slept in a barracks, he could see her turning and turning on her hard little cot, mosquito bitten, sweaty inside the brace. He would steal his father's car, rescue her. Go to her house and confront her parents. He finished the school year with Cs, mowed lawns, drove around aimlessly, the radio loud with songs of love's rise and fall.

Her letter, weeks later, was even more terse. *You are in my thoughts. Here they do not believe in deformity, it being a mark of sin.* In the accompanying photo she was lined up, second row, before the chapel. Everyone alike in khakis, baggy T-shirts that covered their collarbones. Still, it was clear she did not wear the brace. Her face was sunburned, her eyes in a squint. *I have earned privileges, piano hymns during weekday service. So strange to find myself in this place. I'll try to write again. Take care.*

He thought about Moonies, Manson girls, Krishnas with their shaved heads, their robes the orange of prison uniforms. How long would it take?

So strange to find myself. Strange, indeed, his level-headed girl, too smart for tales of angels and clouds, devils with pitchforks, eternal flames. And that word, deformity. Surely she didn't believe such a thing. Because how could her body, her beautiful body which he'd seen and touched, be a mark of sin?

She was crooked was all. Stoop-shouldered, slightly leaning. Without the brace she would become hunched, her ribs weighing on her heart, compressing it. She'd told him that. Had they seized it, locked it away? Tossed it in a bonfire like so much trouble? The week before, he'd had an eye exam and his prescription had been strengthened. Until the eye drops wore off he'd felt vulnerable, the world unfamiliar. In the photo she'd sent no one wore glasses.

Water
The carnival was coming.

All day men worked in the heat of the municipal lot assembling rides from pieces stashed in trailers. The Tilt-A-Whirl, the carousel and Scrambler, he watched them take shape. Games of chance appeared overnight, dartboards, mounted rifles, shelves of plastic-sheathed animals, sad-eyed dogs, benignly smiling lambs.

Late August. He'd not heard from her again. Had he imagined it, their time together, the grave look on her face when they kissed, the taste of cherry Chapstick and the way she'd grab his arm in the movies, her image distinct as ever then wavering, a mirage—he shook his head—a mirage in a sundress splayed with tiny blue flowers?

The carnival's opening night, he'd biked over hoping to meet friends. She was in a group of girls, dowdy ones, some of whom he recognized. She smiled at his approach, excused herself from her gaping companions.

A week, she said, a week she'd been back.

You could've called.

They won't let me use the phone.

Or written.

It was…you don't know. It wasn't like I could just walk to a mailbox.

What was it like then?

Gently he put his hands on her shoulders, claiming her. She kept still, her arms at her sides, her gaze focused on some distant point. She was shorter than he remembered. Her hair, sun bleached and brittle, was clipped back in a way that made her look severe. At her neck a plain gold cross. He toyed with it, rubbed it between his fingers. Who had given it to her?

You don't wear it anymore, he said.

The brace? I told you. I don't have to.

It was not what he meant and he suspected she knew that. He took her hand—briefly she let him—surprised at how soft it was, how tentative her grip. Side by side they walked down the Midway, nodding at acquaintances, answering each other's light questions— his summer was fine, boring really, she'd be back at school, yes, a full schedule. Colored lights flashed, music blared, the air reeked of burnt sugar and grease, molecules refusing to rest in the makeshift, buzzing world. He bought a cotton candy, their lips turning sticky from the treat, and it was all he could to do to keep from kissing her right there on the Midway with everyone to see.

On the Tilt-A-Whirl they pressed their backs to the wall, struggling not to slide to the pit below. The Scrambler felt as if it might just fly apart—one loose nut or bolt to send them careening out to sea. She was thrown against his shoulder then propelled back. All around them were shrieks of mock terror and delight.

They played a game of chance.

He would win something—a kewpie doll, a coin purse, a string of beads; she could count on him. He placed a folded dollar on six, his lucky number, his birth month and date. The barker spun a wheel and the numbers blurred then slowed, ticking past the apex. He tried again, another folded bill. Each mark on the wheel denoted not a number but an ordinary moment from a life barely begun; he imagined them that way. The wheel stopped and he was an old man asleep in rumpled pajamas. Again and he was a baby, screaming for suck. Once more, he saw himself stroking a woman's dark hair as she bent over something. A flower bed? A fussing child? Beneath her thin shirt he could see the perfect knobs of her vertebrae.

They walked away empty-handed.

But there was nothing I wanted, she said. Nothing at all.

At the top of the Ferris wheel their car swayed, pinpricks of lights beneath their feet and the sulfurous whiff of low tide on the breeze. He could just glimpse the sea, a blaze where the sun was low. The mythical place where the earth fell away, where dragons appeared on old maps, a place he could take her where they could be themselves. Win or lose, he had to try his luck, up in the air, finally alone. But she turned her face from his.

No. It's different now.

Different how? We're the same as before.

We're not. She'd folded her hands in her lap and she spoke as if to them. I've been saved, you haven't.

Saved? You don't believe that cartoon shit, do you?

She did not reply. The car began its slow descent. She leaned away from him, serene and aloof, slightly off center. It would get worse, this leaning. Year by year her spine would twist, ribs shifting, pressing the life from her heart. He understood that, even if she did not.

During his eye exam, when he'd looked into the optometrist's machine, the world had gone briefly sharp. Better? the doctor had asked. Fuzzy or clear? For a moment he could see each letter on the chart. Then something clicked, the lenses changed, and the world became indistinct again.

He could not hate her.

Their car had stopped. He thought about chance, the barker's spinning wheel, so much life still to go. He looked at her and felt nothing. He looked out towards the water and saw water. ಐ

Winston Speaks

Jill Caputo

Winston sold candy at the bus station on Wednesdays because that was the only day Georgia could give him a ride there. He kept the goods in the pack on the back of his chair: Snickers, Milky Ways, Reeses Peanut Butter Cups, M&Ms, both peanut and plain. The sign mounted on the back of his chair told his customers what Winston could not: ALL CANDY IN KING SIZE PACKS FOR $1. He was an entrepreneur.

Winston loved the bus plaza. The chipped blue benches, the mock-sparkle concrete floor, the bird-screeching sound of the buses. Even the unrefrigerated water fountain by the stairs. This Wednesday Georgia parked Winston by the center bench, the circular one, where he could watch the people go by. Impatient mothers holding the hands of their children, fat ladies walking with canes, old people carrying groceries, even bums. Winston knew he would stand out to all of them.

Georgia popped open the top of Winston's A&W Root Beer can, and set it in the cup holder on the right side of his chair. She retrieved a straw from her purse and stuck it in the top of the can. Later in the day when it got hot he could lean over and take a sip when he felt like it. She took his body in her hands, pulling him up in his chair by his armpits. He was wearing his red button-up shirt today, and the red-and-white hat he knew she'd always hated, Budweiser plastered across the front of it. She took his head in her hands, slightly ruffling the unshaven whiskers, lifted his hat and pushed his hair back. Her calloused knuckles, the too-small dollar store thumb ring, the nails bitten back so far you could see the skin—Georgia's hands were the part of her Winston knew best.

"I'll be back to get you at five," Georgia said. "I'm sorry it's such a short visit today, but I've just got so much to do."

Winston nodded with his eyes. He watched the full round rump of her ass jiggle away and he wondered what she looked like naked. He couldn't believe he'd never seen her body, even after all this time.

Winston knew Georgia so well by now it was hard to imagine that the first time she had ever given him a bed bath he was actually embarrassed. Newly divorced and fresh out of Certified Nursing Assistant school, Georgia was the sixth nursing assistant Winston had had in a year, but he was her first real patient. He was sick of them coming and going: the pretty ones, the ugly ones, the fat grandmothers who pretended to be nice when they were hired. When they left they all said the same thing, "It's just too depressing. He can't even talk. I don't get paid enough for this kind of job."

Georgia was thirty-four, and while she fell somewhere in the middle of the pretty scale that Winston used to rank his nurse's aides, she talked to him, treated him like he was real. And she explained everything. "I'm going to give you a bed bath, is that okay? I don't want you having to lie here dirty all day."

Winston smiled at her, showing his eye teeth, trying to let her know it was okay.

"The first time I gave someone one of these baths was in CNA training. But then I didn't even have a real person to practice with. I worked on a dummy. I was still married then, to my husband, Tom. He was in the Air Force and never home. Always at the base, always flying planes, always fighting his own personal wars. I was always alone. I think he was having an affair, you know, with another woman. Am I hurting you?"

Georgia had folded the bed sheets to cover most of Winston's nude body while she worked on one limb at a time, dipping the washcloth into a bowl of soapy lukewarm water on the nightstand. She was stroking him up and down, up and down, starting with the corners of his eyes all the way to between his toes. Winston realized how long it had been since he was really clean.

"Tom never wanted me to get my certification. I think he just wanted me to stay at home while he went gallivanting all over the country. Even to other countries. It's what drove us apart. I was too independent. I have to be around people in order to survive."

Her hands were younger then, less calloused, large, but almost delicate. She had shiny pink polish on her nails and her wedding ring was still on her left hand. Winston wondered when she had gotten divorced. It couldn't have been that long ago. He began to see her hands as beautiful, and the lower and lower her hands moved on his body, the more excited he became until he was having a straight-up erection. Part of him hoped Georgia didn't notice, part of him hoped that she did. He wanted her to know that he was a real man.

"Oh!" Georgia said. She looked away from Winston's eyes. "I guess you were even happier to have a bath than I thought you would be." She draped the sheet over Winston's genitals. "I'll just leave you alone for a while." Georgia left the room. Winston breathed in and out to calm himself down. At forty-three, handicapped his entire life, Winston had had thousands of bed baths in his life, but none of them had affected him in this way. That was two years ago.

Max was coming to talk to him now. Winston could see him without turning his head—the small beaky nose, the sharp wrinkled jaw and overbite like the teeth of a rodent. No hair was left on the top of his head, only gray fuzz. Max was Winston's only real friend at the bus station. He was always there on Wednesdays, always with his briefcase, always trying to sell his papers. He never remembered anything he had said to Winston the week before. Winston was surprised he even remembered his name.

"How are you doing there, Old Winston?" Max patted Winston on the shoulder, his body swaying with the movement of his arm. He was old, probably about eighty; so skinny it looked like he was starving. "What bus are you waiting for?" Max should have known by now that Winston never got on any buses. "Me, I'm not going on any bus today. I'm just going to stay here and try to sell my papers. Five dollars each. Wanna buy one?"

Winston shook his head, but Max opened his briefcase anyway. "Did I ever tell you that I got a masters degree in mathematics from the University of Minnesota? That I was going to get my PhD, but my wife got pregnant?" He got out one of his papers and showed it to Winston. The title read, "Proof That God Did Not Create the Universe." Max had shown it to Winston every Wednesday for the past four months. "It can be mathematically proven, you know, even with the help of the Bible. God didn't create shit."

Max sat down on the bench beside Winston. "I've got something for you, Old Winston. I've got something for the both of us." He reached into his shirt pocket and pulled out two fancy Cuban cigars. "What do you say? Let's smoke it up." Winston watched as Max licked the end of one cigar, then the other one too. His sharp teeth moved in a swift motion as he bit off the end of the first cigar and spat it out on the ground. He stuck what was left in Winston's mouth. "Ever smoked a cigar before?" Winston had not. "When I was younger and had a job I used to smoke these things all the time. Used to drive Phyllis crazy." Phyllis was Max's wife; she had left him years ago to pursue her country-western dream in Nashville. Max lit his own cigar with a rusted silver lighter, then leaned over to Winston and did the same for him. "Just hold it in your mouth, boy. Let the ash build up and it will smell and taste real good. Like nothing you've ever done before."

Winston coughed. He let the ash of his cigar build up and up until the sweet and sticky smell overpowered the air all around him, and he'd never felt like such a man before.

The normalcy of Winston's relationship with Georgia was what pleased him so much that first year she worked at his house. Every day it was the same routine. Georgia would get up and get dressed, then she would get Winston ready and up in his chair. Sometimes Georgia would have to leave Winston alone while she went to the supermarket or ran some other errand, but mostly they were together all day, every day. Georgia would talk to him; Georgia would read to him. Winston could read, but he couldn't hold the book. His hands were too shaky. That was part of the problem. Winston couldn't even write because he lacked the fine motor skills. Georgia would cook for them. They would even watch *The Young and the Restless* together every day at noon. Winston couldn't believe how engrossed he became in the soap.

One day, they were watching "their show"—as Georgia called it—when she said something odd. She had her knitting in her lap, a hobby she'd taken up only since Winston had known her. Her fingers worked meticulously on a green and brown thing she had been knitting for over a month. Winston knew it was a scarf for him, meant to protect him from the cold. Her hands looked tired now, the knuckles hard and chafed, the pink polish gone. The wedding ring was gone too. Winston hadn't seen it for months.

When the soap segments were on, they would watch in silence, but during the commercial breaks Georgia would put the TV on mute so she could talk. "Winston," Georgia said, putting her knitting down, "have you ever been in love?"

Winston closed his eyes. He had not been in love, at least not in love with anyone who had been in love with him back.

Georgia kept talking. "I mean, really in love, so in love that you felt like there was no one else left in the world? That you'd found your soul mate? That's how I felt when I first met Tom. Every moment I was with him I was giggling and happy and I didn't want to be anywhere else. But then everything just went wrong. Things just got too quiet. No communication. I think true love is constant even in silence."

Winston shifted his weight in his chair. Suddenly every part of Georgia seemed to be speaking to him, from her peroxide blond hair to the laugh wrinkles around her mouth and eyes, to the constant movement of her hands. They were both lonely people, but they needed each other. Why else would she say such things to him?

Five months into the first year that had Georgia moved in with Winston to take care of him, it snowed. The house Winston lived in was small, just one level, and two bedrooms, with doorways he could barely get his chair through. Winston's house was paid for by his disability check, but it was falling apart. The toilet leaked when somebody flushed it too hard, the stove wouldn't turn off once it was turned on, and the heater was temperamental. Georgia's room was on the other side of the house, but when Winston heard a knock on his door at 2:45 a.m., he wasn't that surprised. He hadn't been sleeping. Just thinking.

"Can I come in?" Georgia said. She was wearing her Snoopy nightgown with the bows that tied at the shoulders; her bare feet scuffled on the hard floor. She walked over to Winston, and even by the soft light of the nightlight he could see the circles under her eyes. "I can't get the heater to turn on in my room. It's freezing in there—you know how it gets, with all the windows exposed to the wind from the street. Do you mind if I sleep with you, just for tonight?"

Winston wouldn't have said no if he could have. His bed was too large for just him; there was plenty of room for the both of them. They could sleep without touching. Georgia got in, always polite, on the opposite side, and slept. But there was no sleep for Winston. He could feel his whole body, tight and contracted, almost pulsing with the presence of her. Winston was a virgin, but he was almost positive everything worked right because he'd had wet dreams before. What if Georgia thought he wasn't capable? She knew him better than anybody else, but what if she thought he wasn't able to perform? Or worse, what if he ejaculated in his sleep?

By morning nothing had happened, except she was much closer to him, her arms flailed out around his shoulders and the round of her breasts next to the curve in his back. Winston blinked his eyes. He was tired and sleepless, but happy, happier than he'd felt in a long time.

Georgia got up. "Are you awake, Winston? I'm going to make us something warm to eat. This is the kind of day you want to stay inside." She walked to the window and opened the shades, pulled back the curtains. The bright white of the snow outside was almost painful; the sun glinting off it created a fire in Winston's eyes. "It's white, like Christmas," she said. But it was still only October, not even Halloween. Georgia slept in Winston's bed for the rest of the winter.

Although he loved the bus station, Winston was scared of the buses. On the platform of the bus station, with the power on his wheelchair off, he was safe, but he always had some fear of falling off, of hitting his joystick with the edge of his elbow and speeding out into the street where the buses would smash him. He'd thought about getting on a bus; he knew they were all handicapped accessible, some with lifts, some with ramps. But the problem was there was nowhere to go—if he got on, where would he get off? What if he got lost? Occasionally one of the friendlier drivers would offer Winston a ride, but Winston always shook his head. Today when Winston's favorite driver, Bess, came round, she opened the doors of Bus Number Three as if to invite Winston in. "How you doing today, Winston? How about a ride?"

Max answered for him. "He can't get on your bus. At least not today, woman. Old Winston has too much business to take care of right here. Too much candy to sell." Max patted the pack on the back of Winston's chair. "Isn't that right, Winston?"

Winston nodded, relieved.

The spring of their first year together had been the happiest time for Winston. It was warm outside, but not too hot, and on most days Georgia would take Winston outside. They would sit together on the small cracked patch of cement that served as Winston's backyard patio, Georgia reading to him or sometimes even singing—her alto voice squeaked on the high-pitched notes, but Winston didn't mind. She would feed him slices of oranges and pieces of watermelon with the seeds already carefully taken out— she didn't want Winston to choke. And she would talk about her life, what it had been like before she'd met Winston—how much taking care of him had helped her grow as a person.

Summer had been much the same, only hotter, which meant more time spent indoors, but when the fall came around again and the weather got cooler, Winston noticed a change in Georgia, as if she had gotten cooler too, more distant. In her eyes, Winston often saw she was thinking about something far away. When she spoke, it was almost deliberate; she chose her words carefully.

She was getting Winston dressed for the day when she first brought up the idea. Pulling the T-shirt over his head, working his arms through the armholes. "Winston," she said, "have you ever thought about getting another aide?"

Winston instinctively jerked back, his eyes growing big; Georgia recognized the panic in them. "Don't worry," she said, "I'm not abandoning you. I just thought it might be nice to have someone else who could help out too. A second aide who could maybe help you do some little things, get you showered and in bed at night. I'd still be here too. And with someone else to help with the bothersome things, you and I could spend more quality time together during the day. Plus, I'd like to go back to school and get my LPN license. And most of those classes are at night."

It wasn't long after that conversation that Winston fell. He had been trying to pour himself a glass of grape juice. He didn't try to do things like this very often, but Georgia was gone so long that day that he'd gotten impatient, and thirsty. Georgia had left Winston in his power chair so that could go anywhere in the house that he wanted. Winston knew that the grape juice was on the bottom shelf of the fridge and that he could reach it if he could get the refrigerator door open. Opening the door was easy, but the shelf was lower than he had expected. When he leaned forward there was nothing to keep him in his chair except for his hands, which instead of reacting quickly, decided to tremor.

Initially Winston tried to get up, using his hands like tiny claws and trying to bend his knees so that he could raise up on them, but the more he twisted and turned the more uncomfortable he became, and the more he thought about it, the more pointless his situation seemed. He could never get up by himself.

The linoleum floor of the kitchen was harder than Winston had thought it would be. From his chair, and under his wheels, the linoleum had seemed soft, almost malleable. But lying on the floor, the top of his body curled in a tight ball and his legs bent back under him, wedged between the kitchen table and the refrigerator, Winston felt there was nothing in the world more solid than the floor. Or more cold. His legs began to grow numb from lack of blood flow; his shirt was twisted up around his armpits.

When he could no longer feel his legs, he closed his eyes and thought of Georgia. Soon she would be home—any time now for sure, and when she saw Winston lying on the floor she would scoop him up in her arms and hug him. She would rub his arms and legs and maybe even kiss him on the forehead. Winston could almost feel her warmth.

When Georgia did come home, she almost stepped on Winston. She was carrying paper bags from the store, and wearing a mini skirt, which Winston thought was strange. She didn't even notice Winston until she went to put something away in the fridge, and then, there he was.

"Winston!" she said, just missing him with her left foot, but her voice wasn't kind and soothing like he expected it to be. She seemed annoyed. "What the in the hell are you doing down there?" Georgia had hardly ever cussed around Winston; she seemed to have endless patience with him. "You know you really shouldn't try to do things by yourself. You might really get hurt and I won't be responsible for it. What if something had happened to me, and I didn't make it home? I could have gotten held up; I could have gotten in a car wreck. There are millions of things that could have happened to me, and then what would have happened to you?"

Her eyes were big and watery as she lifted Winston roughly up by the armpits and sat him down his chair. She took a dishtowel that was hanging over the edge of the sink and wiped her eyes with it. "I have too much stress in my life for this, Winston."

Winston didn't know the name of the old homeless woman who lived in the bus plaza, and he didn't think Max did either. She sat in the corner, by the restrooms, and yelled things at people walking by. Her hair was tied back with a ratty yellow bandana; her cheekbones— harsh and sharp from malnutrition—had black smudges on them. She was always sipping on something, from a thermos. Max said it was whiskey to keep her warm, and that he hated her.

Today Max was bothering the homeless lady because, it seemed to Winston, there was nothing else to do. Winston watched as Max walked over and sat down on the ground beside her, trying to talk to her. Max opened his briefcase and pulled out his paper. He showed it to the lady, talking about God and the universe again. Winston watched as the woman snatched the paper out of Max's hands, ripping it in half. "Fucking moron!" she yelled at Max. "Fucking waste of God's time!" She leapt back, taking the pieces of paper with her.

"Give me that back, bitch! That's valuable property!" Max began chasing the woman, hobbling around on his stumpy old legs and dragging his briefcase behind him; they circled the bus plaza until they came right up next to Winston and stopped. The homeless woman was much younger than Winston had thought from a distance, probably in her early forties.

"You and your papers," she said to Max. "You and your papers nobody wants to buy! You're just an old man who has nothing better to do than talk to a cripple!" She looked at Winston. "Fucking cripple riding around in your goddamn chariot! If I had my way, I'd throw you out into the street!"

Winston watched as Max pulled back from the homeless woman, raised his hand, and with as much force as his bony frame could muster, slapped her across the cheek. The homeless lady, gasping, knelt down on the ground.

"Don't you ever talk like that about my friend Winston! He has a name, you know, and he's a lot more capable than you." Max walked over to Winston, abandoning the homeless lady and even the pieces of paper that were now scattered all over the ground.

Eventually Georgia apologized for the way she had acted when she found Winston on the floor. She said that she had gotten in an argument with her sister, Lorna, earlier in the day and that traffic had been terrible on her way home from the store. But even after the apology, Winston still saw Georgia differently. She never called him a cripple to his face, but he began to think she thought of him as one. And she stopped talking so much. Sometimes she barely talked to him at all. They spent whole dinners in silence.

Winston couldn't figure it out. For some reason Georgia was *mad* at him. Now Georgia used words for business matters only.

"Winston, I'm making you macaroni and cheese for dinner."

"Winston, your dinner is done." Georgia shoveled the macaroni and cheese into a bowl in front of Winston. On days when Winston felt good, he liked to try and feed himself. He had gotten better at it since Georgia had been with him, but only because she had constantly encouraged him.

Now as he reached for the spoon to put into the bowl, Georgia gave him a hasty look. The journey from the bowl to Winston's mouth was a laborious one, and Winston missed. Georgia let out a big sigh. "Just let me do it for you, Winston. You're going to make a huge mess."

"Don't let that crazy old broad get to you," Max told Winston. "She wouldn't know a real cripple if she saw one. Crazy homeless bitch. Listen, don't ever let anyone call you crippled, Winston, or even handicapped. You're physically challenged, that's all. You just have limitations." He slapped Winston on the back. "Did I ever tell you about the day I had to put my little Peggy in a home? She was mentally handicapped. Retarded, you know. Had the mind of a four-year-old. We took care of her ourselves for as long as we could, but when she got older it was just too much for Phyllis to handle by herself. We had to put her in a home. Sunflower Lane, it was called. Real nice joint. I visited her every day for years." Max put his hands on his knees, leaning over, real close to Winston's face. "Anyway, my point is, no matter what someone calls you, crippled or whatever, at least you're doing something for yourself. At least you're out here in the world."

Things between Winston and Georgia never got better. He began to look at her as someone who was scared, overwhelmed; someone who saw him as helpless and handicapped. But this only made him want her more. Now he spent most of his time thinking about Georgia, even when she wasn't at home. He thought of all the good times they'd had together; the fact that Georgia was the closest thing to a real woman or relationship that he'd ever had. The beginning with Georgia was the happiest Winston had ever been in his life, and he wanted that back. He was scared of her leaving. She was on the phone all the time now, talking to her sister, who lived in Florida. Winston thought she had a boyfriend. He wondered what the boyfriend looked like, where Georgia met him, and if she went to see the boyfriend when she left sometimes at night. Other nights Winston overheard Georgia's conversations when he was supposed to be sleeping.

"Honestly, Lorna, there's got to be some other way." Georgia was crying. "He's just so sweet, and little, but I don't get paid enough, and even the heater doesn't work."

Winston began to see that for Georgia, living with him was just another job.

"Yes. But he's always trying to do things for himself, and if something happens to him, I don't want to be the one to blame. Budd says I should move in with him; he says he has enough money to support the both of us for a while."

The next day Georgia was gone all day, and she didn't tell Winston where she was going. She just left him in the bed. No matter. It wasn't like Winston had never done anything for himself before he'd had an aide like Georgia who he depended on so totally. And with Georgia becoming so distant, Winston had become wily, figuring things out for himself. He had discovered a way to get out of situations such as this. His chair was parked parallel to his bed. He flipped himself over onto his side, with his arms, which were stronger than the rest of his body. He lay there, paused in slow motion, and in movements he considered as lovely as ballet, he flipped himself into his chair.

In the kitchen, where he was getting something to eat, Winston saw papers. Newspapers, and ads. Job ads circled in red: pediatric nurse's aide, nursing home attendant, even an ad for a receptionist at a beauty salon. Georgia really was leaving him. Winston squeaked in panic, and his whole body stiffened, his legs shooting out from their place on the footrests. His fingers extended to graze the edges of the newspaper. Paper cuts, bleeding.

That was yesterday, Tuesday. Now it was 4:45 on Wednesday. Soon Georgia would be coming to pick him up from the bus station to take him home, maybe for the very last time. Winston breathed, took a swig of this root beer, thirst and saliva coming out of his mouth. Max was asleep on the bench beside him, snoring. Winston thought Max might die any day, probably where he was right now, in the bus plaza. Awake or asleep, it didn't matter; Max had lived a long life.

It was amazing, Winston thought. He was only forty-five, but he felt as old as Max. He was forty-five, but he had the experience of an adolescent boy. He pondered these contradictions, and he mulled over the past two years he'd spent with Georgia. How quickly the time had passed, but how much their relationship had changed, until it was less than a relationship at all, he decided. The Georgia of now was just an acquaintance.

Winston heard a screech, a clicking sound, and he knew at once the sound of Bus Number Three, and Bess, coming back to the station for the fourth time today. He saw the girl on the side of the bus eating the Subway sandwich, and her whole face seemed to smile directly at him. He wasn't scared anymore. He thought of Georgia and the red circled job ads, the late-night phone conversations. Georgia in the bed with him, Georgia feeding him macaroni and cheese, Georgia leaving him, Georgia fucking another man.

The doors of the bus swung open, and somehow Winston found himself right in front of them. He looked at Bess and her great heaving body, her gray hair hanging down in her eyes, the coffee cup in her hand. She smiled at him. "Hey, Winston," she said. "Do you want to get on my bus or what?"

And this time, Winston got on. ∞

Climacteric

Cynthia Neely

You woke today to an ache
you thought was spent—that season
already mourned and set aside,
flushed away like pink-tinged tissue.

It's a late-March-snow in February, far
too early to be so transient; yet
its whitewash is not unwelcome to the grime
of the fading season. Even now,

as wasps stumble out of the woodwork, fumble
drunken and useless on gray stone floors, winter
begins its end, always before you are ready, always
before your mind has softened

to the idea of it. You hold on too long,
as if letting go will lose…what?
The clean and cold, the muffled
and muffed, safely layered in wool and white?

Or the weightlessness that comes with snow?
It's not that you dread the beginning
of the new, but the ending
of the old. Still you lighten your step

when the earth is young, green rising,
and despair spring petals' fade.
You bask in the heat of long days,
relish the taste of salt, then miss the sweat of it

in coming shadows. How you whistle
so you can see your breath
in the first frost of fall, but grieve
that last leaf's bright tumble.

        ಐ

Rest Hour on the Southfield Ferry, circa 1912

The Southfield Ferry was moored on the East River behind Bellevue Hospital, and served as an outpatient preventorium for pretubercular patients (those infected with tuberculosis but without clinical symptoms).

The Bellevue Preventorium was one of the few tuberculosis treatment programs that was fully integrated. Even in the north, most preventoria and sanatoria remained segregated.

Cats were ubiquitous at Bellevue until the mid-1970s, tolerated by the administration mainly for their mice-hunting skills. Though the formal pet-therapy movement did not arise until the 1960s, generations of Bellevue patients found comfort and companionship in this feline presence.

When the WPA commissioned the FDR Drive—the highway that now runs along Manhattan's east side—the ferries outside Bellevue were scrapped. (The cover photo of ambulances was taken just prior to ground-breaking for the highway.) By then, the Bellevue C&D Building had opened, with loggia for the required sunshine and fresh air, so ferries were no longer needed. Of course, once the antibiotic INH became available for TB treatment in 1951, the loggia were deemed unnecessary. Today, it is rare for hospitalized patients to have access to fresh air.

Photo courtesy of Bellevue Hospital Center Archives

Happiness Advocates

B.G. Firmani

My friend Wei was telling me about how he used to go to a social anxiety support group, but it eventually collapsed because the people in the group had too much social anxiety. I told him that sort of reminded me of going to my monthly stuttering support group and how, sometimes, after a long, exhausting day, during the sharing session I would just want people to spit it the eff out already. I knew it was bad but sometimes it was just too much for me.

We had a gig together, one of these "creative team" deals I'd found on Craigslist, Wei the designer, I the copywriter, on which we'd foolishly underbid—this being deep in the recession, we'd figured we'd need to go pretty low to be considered at all. Never, ever bid lump-sum had always been the advice given me by my older and savvier mentors, but that's just what we'd done, and now Wei and I were toiling like indentured servants, working for the equivalent of about $19.50 an hour, split two ways. We'd met the year before, at a Taiwanese cosmetics company where Wei was the only guy and I was the only non-Asian; somehow us both being "exceptions" had created a keen bond between us, and we'd decided to throw in our lot together.

This new gig was near Chinatown, which at least meant we could get cheap eats for lunch, and so we'd go off to places like Noodle Village or Vegetarian Dim Sum House and get some hearty and filling food for a few sweaty dollars. Vegetarian Dim Sum always had Buddhist "literature," in Chinese, by the door, and one day a box of golden, woven strings appeared beside the pamphlets. *Blessed bracelets,* a sign read, *free*—actually, Wei had to translate it for me—and we each picked one out and took turns tying them on each other's wrists. Then we walked back to work with tears in our eyes, moved by this unexpected largesse.

It really was a weird gig and after we signed on (our eyes on the prize, as it were, of the $4,000 fee), we found our employers quickly morphing from a sort of benign, dealing-with-clinical-depression organization—they were called "Happiness Advocates"—to what seemed to us an actively pernicious, if not downright crazy, group of evangelical Christians. For these people we were spending our days in a crummy little workroom furnished with taken-out-of-the-trash-after-a-fire-at-Office-Depot furniture, churning out massive "decks" of PowerPoint slides. We sat elbow to elbow, Wei speed-cropping his way through tens of thousands of inspirational images of puppies, kittens, newborn babies, and masses of little blond children playing in fields, the sun over the trees behind them doing a '70s-cinema-style lens flare. Meanwhile it was my task to make into something like English the chunks of text that had been put through an electronic translator and yielded things that read like Language poetry:

> *The five ice-skates will increase to the throne that remembers the conclusion of your suffering, displeasure and confirmed pain because. It transports difficulty and where it is disappointing reassuring it dates a joy. Me heaven Chopped herbs; this the morning hatches have demanded it new. My child!*

As the amount of work in the project grew in sneaky and dispiriting ways (scope "creep" this is called, probably for a reason), I tried to negotiate for more pay. I was told by the production manager there, a testy lady named Shu who suffered from heel spurs, that there was nothing she could do and I'd have to speak with Fred, the man who had hired us. However, Fred's attendance in the offices of the organization proved elusive, like a sighting of the Snuffleupagus. I left notes and phone messages for him—hell for a person who stutters, let it be said—and sent him emails, and even went so far as to tape a letter written in Sharpie on a piece of tabloid-sized paper to where the seam of his office door met its jamb so that, like a cop at a crime scene, I could later see if the seal had been broken. Needless to say, nothing worked. Finally one day as I was coming back from the ladies' room I saw Fred himself turning a corner, silent and stealthy in his crepe-soled desert boots. I raced down the hall after him.

"You'd sssssssaid three thousand images, ffffffffifty 'decks' of thirty sssssslides—and there's easily uh, uh, uh four or maybe six times that," I said. There were actually five times that, but "five" is a word I always block on.

Fred tilted his head to the side, reacting, as some people will do, more to my stutter than the content of my speech. I was still trying to talk but he smiled at me and said in incredibly nice tones:

"The Lord will provide."

He had a Charismatic Leader way about him, so I was thrown for a moment. Also, there's something about a man gazing soulfully into your eyes, even if he looks like Dick Van Dyke, which makes you less inclined to want to argue with him. When I recovered, Fred had disappeared down the hall like a slinky cat burglar. I raced after him, but when I turned the corner the elevator door had closed with a needlessly cheerful electronic bell ring.

How could I let this happen? I felt bad mostly for Wei, because he was a good twelve years younger than I, and I felt like this whole sour gig with the Christians was my fault. I should have been more protective of him.

"It's okay," Wei said in that kind, slightly saddened way of his when I told him what happened with Fred. That's the problem with us, I thought, sinking back in my seat; we were both raised religious so we know how to eat shit. Wei went back to cropping, I went back to Englishing, and another day of futility quietly passed.

Months of tight-deadline gigs such as this one had made Wei and me nearly immune to each other's weirdnesses. For instance, we were both mad hair-twirlers, and when Wei was going to town on a particular worry spot with one of his hands, the marvel for me was that he could cover the keyboard with the other—he had stretchy, girlish hands with slightly knobby knuckles—with absolutely no diminution of his productivity level. Meanwhile besides the stutter and my own relentless hair-twirling I made all kinds of energetic mouth noises when I was copy-editing, a bit like Mose Allison rocking out to his own piano playing. But we were just fine with each other, and it was actually heartening to think that a twenty-five-year-old gay fellow from deepest rural China and a thirty-seven-year-old nerdishly intellectual daughter of a bookie from south Philly could be so utterly comfortable with each other, almost like we were two halves of the same person.

We talked all the time. Wei had been in Europe for three years and this country for eight so he was really cosmopolitan, and he told me everything there was to know about popular clothing styles seen at the USCIS office, Italian adaptations of Chengdu-style Sichuan cooking, and gay sex. Meanwhile, he was all ears for my sundry disquisitions on string theory, the Oxford comma, and the essays of Robert Warshow. Together, we could be specific. Wei was more fearless than I as far as dating was concerned, however; come the weekend, I would be on the train back up to Inwood, to my books and my DVD library and my cat, a creature rather like Wei in that she didn't appear to notice if I stuttered, whereas Wei's dance card would be full. As time went on, one of his many fellows started to separate from the pack. Halloween came about a week before the time when our gig was supposed to wrap up and, in expectation of our paycheck, Wei went to Ricky's to buy himself an outfit to surprise this special boyfriend with. The salesgirl asked Wei what he had in mind, and sweet, sylph-like Wei, looking at the Bat Girl and Madame du Barry and Miss Mouse outfits, said:

"Something slutty."

He settled on a French Maid costume, and would only say the Monday afterwards that his boyfriend had *really, really* liked it. Unfortunately for us, as we were talking we heard a sharp intake of breath and turned to see Shu in the doorway, spying on us. She opened her religious mouth to say something, but then thought better—despite my unflaggingly nerdy credentials I actually look like a person who could slam the shit out of you—and turned and limped away, the severity of her heel spurs being dependent on how put-upon she thought she needed to appear to her staff. Clearly Shu thought Wei and I were a couple of freaks to begin with, but this incident put us both on a gloomy path and we were uncharacteristically quiet for the rest of the afternoon.

Worst of all for me, if I don't keep my instrument tuned up, as it were, my stutter comes back in an extra-strength form the longer I keep silent. And so, in parting with Wei that evening, I wasn't even able to warble out a simple "See you later" or even a little "Bye." I opened my mouth, nothing came out, and I just stood there for a moment staring at him miserably. Wei reached out and squeezed my hand.

It might have been this sad end to the day that put me in mind of going to a church after work; a strange notion, given my lapsed state. There is nothing like twelve years of Catholic school to make a church hater out of someone. My oldest brother, a religious fanatic and gay-baiting jerk to whom I hadn't spoken at that point for nearly seven years, had in his sarcastic (and highly preferable) youth characterized mass as: *Stand up/ Sit down/ Eat a cookie.* I had of course agreed with him. Despite all this, I found myself slipping inside a church on Catherine Street.

A mass was going on, a fact that I found depressing and intrusive. I sat down in the back and looked up at the ceiling. I realized it was one of the Holy Days of Obligation, a dreadful series of words, and this must be the one where you prayed for "the souls of the faithful departed" who were imperfect. Because of this imperfection, these souls were stuck in Purgatory. I sat there considering that my mother Rachaele was probably far up the spheres with the harp-playing angels (considering that heaven was a cross between Dante and a *New Yorker* cartoon) and had no need of my prayers, while I was quite sure my dad Pep was still on some viewless terrace in Purgatory, slicing garlic with a single-edge razor as it were, and I thought he should maybe stay there a while longer so that he could fully contemplate what a violent and overbearing asshole he had been in life. So instead of praying for anyone else, I prayed for myself.

I prayed for normalcy, just as I had when I was a child. Years ago I had found the name of the patron saint of stutterers: Notkat Bulbulus. Sometimes called Notker Balbulus. Needless to say, this was a terrible, stupid name to have to pray to. In time I found myself not praying so much as spacing out. And then I was thinking about Wei, who had been raised by harrowing bible-thumpers. He had told me, *Yeah, they believe in Satan and devils and witches on brooms.* They would be at the I-Hop in Fair Lawn, New Jersey, and the pancake combo would come and the parents would start speaking in tongues over the strawberry slices, their way of saying grace. Wei's sister Kelly would join in, and Wei would stare at the ceiling and think of Tom of Finland. His father had literally thrown him out a window when he found out he was gay, and Kelly had once actively crossed the street to avoid running into him—holding hands, as he had been, with a young man in a Lady Gaga T-shirt—and having to acknowledge him as her brother in front of her friends. Wei was inured against slights. What he wasn't inured against was sweetness, I thought. Like me, show him the smallest kindness and he turns into a giant mushball.

I said a prayer for Wei and then got up and left.

The next day there was a trash fire on the A line, and I was a little late getting down to Happiness Advocates. I rang up but no one buzzed me in; thankfully, there were other businesses in the building, and a gruff man who worked for the travel agency on the second floor held the door for me. And then as soon as the elevator, with its offensively cheerful electronic chirrup, opened on our floor, I realized it was all over.

Wei was sitting on the windowsill as if he had been dropped there like a ragdoll. What was amazing was that every last computer, chair, stick of shitty furniture, and even unloved potted office rubber tree plant was gone. Everything. We looked at each other and I marched through the room and pushed open the door to our workroom—empty. I crossed the room, Wei saying "Don't bother, don't bother," and pushed open Heel Spur Woman's door—the same thing, empty. I turned and looked at him.

"Those fuckers," he said.

"Those fffffuckers," I agreed.

We stood staring at each other, our four thousand dollars flying out of the room like a wicked little ha-ha parrot.

"I can't believe I spent my last fifty bucks on a French Maid outfit," Wei said. Then he began to cry.

I went over to him and put my arms around him and then I found myself crying as well. It was all too much.

We were crying and we were full of lamentations. Why didn't we check them out? Why didn't we Google them or check with the Better Business Bureau or whatever the eff people do, why didn't we ask to see their certificate of whatever it would be, incorporation, why? We were yelling; we blew our noses loudly on the napkins from Chop't Salad that I had in my bag and then we had to look at the printing on the napkins and say Chop't, Chop't, how stupid is that? Chop't Salad, Chop't Salad, how stupid is that? And then we were back to crying again and it was clear that there was nothing to be done, so we left the building.

We didn't have any kind of plan and we didn't know which way we were going, so we crossed the street by Dr. Toothy's, and then found ourselves on Park Row, but the barricades they'd put up by the police station after September 11th made us feel like criminals, so we stumbled down Worth Street. There was the park where you very often see diminutive old folks doing tai chi in the morning, and it was here where we fell onto a bench.

We cried more, lamented loudly, blew our noses. Wei leaned forward, holding a Chop't Salad napkin up in front of his face and staring at it fiercely. I took one and ripped its edge and pulled the two plys apart, something my mother had instructed me to do as a child, to make paper products last longer, and blew my nose. I slowly realized it was an almost preternaturally nice day outside, early autumn, uncharacteristically warm but with a cool breeze.

"Ha," Wei said, "'Happiness Advocates.' We should have known."

"Yeah, what kind of a na-na-na-um-name is that?" I said.

"I hope they rot in hell," he said.

We sat there for a while, like an old, indigent, long-married couple enjoying the sun, which was at least free.

"Wei," I said, "I'm sssssso sssssorry I got you into this."

He sat up and flipped his hair out of his eyes.

"It's not your fault," he said. "Don't worry. Next time we'll know to check."

I felt my tears start to come back, and he took my hand and waggled it for a moment. We found ourselves looking down, at the lucky golden bracelets on our wrists.

"Ha," I said, "lu-lu-lucky."

"We'll just check next time," he repeated.

I was stuttering up a storm but really we were just talking and I realized that I was strangely elated to hear my young friend talk about "next time." We had both been through some shit, I thought. The sun felt good on my arms and I realized, of course we'd go on. What other option did we have? We were tough as nails, our tribe—the freaks, the weirdos, the stutterers. We'd been through so much that really nothing could touch us. I turned to Wei whose eyes were closed. His head was thrown back against the bench, and he was enjoying the sun on his sweet face. He must have sensed me looking at him because he opened his eyes and turned to me, not speaking.

Go on, he said with his eyes, *I am listening.* ☙

To Melancholia, Mon Amour

Nancy Naomi Carlson

Because I want to leave you
something beautiful, I will dye these sheaves of silk
blood red. You'll see them billow and rise
between pairs of stage hands—Handel's *Israel in Egypt*—

parting the sea as easy as stripping a bed.

I will make of these plagues a tapestry
thick with must and the pale infusion of moon,

or better still, a double choir—for beasts and boils,
frogs and diamonds of hail.

Let me go, and I'll rosin my bow for the whirr of flies,
or the wheels of your chariot in pursuit—
stallions black as the growing dark—

or my heart, straining like locust wings.

&

"Photographs of the Saint's Finger are Strictly Prohibited"

Convent of St. Teresa, Ávila, Spain

Katherine Durham Oldmixon

Her gaze guides our mortal eyes
as if we too could peer through the sun
to record the vision with a feather

like the one poised in her sculpted hand.
But we have come to see the finger—
from her right hand, a roll of bony lace

at last at rest in its gold and glass glove
after lifelong journeys on a priest's breast—
now separate from her transverberated heart

and the arm they cut, after the finger,
revealing her body still uncorrupt
when it bled the medieval must of roses.

After the church men sawed off a foot,
her other arm, a sliver of her jaw, bits
of flesh—there must be an inventory—

they reburied what remained.
Here we are only for that finger
whose sometime tremble was, in their eyes,

the vital sign in her three-year coma. How
they must have watched it flicker on her bed
until it became the girl and all the body they could bear.

∞

In a Time of Scars

Gaynell Gavin

What stays with you latest and deepest?
- Walt Whitman, "The Wound-Dresser"

First, I believed I could fly. At four, jumping from my aunt's bed, I flew into the corner of her nightstand, splitting my forehead. That small, vertical first scar between my eyebrows eventually grew faint.

Fourteen years after my preschool flight, when Joe and I married, I still believed I could beat any odds unscathed. I was wrong again. As 1971 ended, my parents sent gifts, and called to wish us a Merry Christmas, but they were not happy I'd dropped out of college two months earlier, married a black guy, and become a white speck in the midst of Roxbury.

Joe's family gathered at his great-aunt Grace's in Cambridge after Christmas dinner. As we clambered into her elegant townhouse, stomping snow, shedding coats, scarves, and gloves, Joe's uncle Claude put his arm around my shoulders. He was an engineer who lived near us, evidently preferring to remain in Roxbury, rather than moving to Cambridge or another rich community. His wife, Leah, taught at the elementary school by our house, a good school, one of the better ones in Roxbury. Now, Claude kissed my cheek, shook Joe's hand, and asked how I liked Boston.

"It's too cold."

"You came to the wrong place. We have nine months of winter here and one of each of the other seasons." Claude took our coats and headed for a bedroom while Joe guided me into a formal living room. His great aunt's presence dominated, making the few other relatives seated in the room a blur. Aunt Grace's chair had a rounded back and was upholstered in dark rust velvet, from which she turned her dignified gaze on me. Her face beneath white hair was very light brown like Claude's, Leah's, their children's, and the faces of the family's New York-DC contingency—the stockbrokers and Howard University professors. "Hello." Grace's voice was as cool as her palm when she took my hand for a moment.

Scrutinized and evidently found wanting, I did manage to say, "I'm pleased to meet you." Joe and I escaped the living room formality, entering the dining room where I met Aunt Professor and Uncle Stockbroker, who sat at the head of a long, cherry table, calling off Bingo numbers. Claude, Leah, Joe's mother Rosie, Joe's stepfather and grandfather sat around the table, eating fruitcake and drinking eggnog, while they played. Aunt Grace entered for a brief goodnight before retreating to her upstairs apartment, while Joe and I excused ourselves to watch TV.

"Maybe you shouldn't touch Grace's television," Aunt Professor warned.

"Oh come on," Claude snapped at her. "Even her TV has an on and off button just like every other TV in the whole wide world. I think they can handle it."

I was beginning to like that man. We headed for the television, switched on an overhead bedroom light and pushed aside some coats, clearing space to sit on the bed, leaning back against the headboard. Joe put his arm around my shoulders, and we watched for a while until his mother called us to come see the slides from her vacation.

Unfortunately for me, Rosie's vacation had been a visit with her older son Randy, who had written a post-vacation letter telling Joe that he had married "one of white America's mistakes." Seeing huge, living color pictures of Randy and his family flash across the wall, splashing Mississippi greenery, was not my idea of a good time: Randy in his new backyard with his new wife, Kaye, and her two little girls a couple of weeks before the birth of their new daughter, Randi Kaye; Randy leaning against his new metallic blue station wagon; Randy pouring drinks at the bar in his rec room in his new house; Randy silhouetted dramatically against a levee as the sun set. Randy's appearances on the wall were met with murmurs of approval from his extended family. There were old slides too: Rosie laughing under an obsolete "Colored Only" restroom sign; Grampie and Rosie, laughing in a cotton field, holding up pods of cotton.

That night, when we entered the bedroom that had been his since childhood, Joe switched on the overhead light and pulled me to him, but I pushed away. "Hey, are you mad at me?"

"Not really." I sat down on the edge of the bed and stared at the pale walls, then at the light hardwood floor. I liked the contrast between the floor and the dark, burnished wood of the stairway banisters. "I'm just mad in general, and you're the only one around to take it out on." Malcolm X, Eldridge Cleaver, Huey Newton, H. Rap Brown, and Ho Chi Minh stared back at me from black-and-white posters on the walls. "I can't stand these men watching me." I jumped up and started tugging down the posters.

Joe laughed and helped me take them down, scraping some of the tape off the walls with his fingernails. When we finished, he rolled them into a cylinder, and stuck them in the closet. He turned and faced me. "Feel better?"

I shrugged. "Sort of."

"That's good because I have something to tell you." He stretched out on the bed with his hands under his head.

"What?"

"You were designed with me in mind."

I told him not to try making me laugh when I'm mad, but then I laughed anyway and sat down beside him while he said, "Seriously, I want to ask you something."

"What?"

"You saw how light my cousins are, how light a lot of my family is."

"Yeah."

"When we were little, we'd get Christmas presents from our relatives in Cambridge, but Claude's kids always got more than

Randy and me. A lot more. It was noticeable. I think it's because their dad didn't leave, and ours did. I think that embarrassed my relatives. But I also think it's because they're lighter and we're darker. What do you think?"

I pulled my legs onto the bed, drew my knees to my chest, and leaned against the cool window, feeling cold air at its edges. I looked out to the near-vacant lot at the end of Waumbeck Street, at the small patch of concrete with a basketball hoop that then sloped sharply upward to the school where Leah taught. Silvery light reflected from the snow.

I turned to Joe. His skin was the color of coffee with only a little cream in it. I looked at his Afro, which was short and soft, at his dark eyes with thick lashes, the details of his eyebrows, the small hockey-puck scar on his forehead from when he refused to wear a mask at fourteen because he wanted everyone to know who was goalie. I traced the scar with my fingers. Finally, I answered him. "I don't know, sweetheart. I don't know why they did what they did or what they think, but I think you're beautiful." I leaned over and kissed the scar.

Just as Boston almost convinced me that Sartre could be wrong—that hell is not necessarily always other people, but can be, instead, unending winter—Louise came to Roxbury, and the first softness of spring in the winter air followed. Louise was married to Joe's stepbrother, Young Gil. He'd been drafted to Vietnam after graduating Boston University. He ended up in military intelligence, and Louise was a secretary at the American embassy in Saigon when they met. Their marriage was not a small feat, given her parents' initial opposition to having a black guy in the family, and obstacles the U.S. government put in the paths of servicemen who tried to marry Vietnamese women.

After his tour of duty ended, Young Gil stayed in Vietnam with Louise, working for one of the American corporations that raked in profits from the war's construction contracts. Once, I heard his dad, Gil, laugh about how Louise's family might not have wanted her to marry a black guy but "didn't mind at all when that black guy saved their necks by helping them get out of the country."

Louise came to Roxbury two months ahead of Young Gil because she was pregnant. The Sunday after she arrived, I listened to the sound of voices around the big mahogany dining room table and watched her. Louise was in her mid-twenties, quiet and small, not visibly pregnant. Her dark hair was long. The faint scar on her cheek, where a plate glass window had shattered in her face when the American embassy was attacked, had healed beautifully and was almost invisible.

The more I watched her, the more I understood that, however quiet, Louise was smart and strong. Weeks passed, her pregnancy became obvious, the air sweetened and warmed, days grew longer, the yards and parks of Roxbury greened. After dinner, Joe and I walked in the parks where drummers and listeners gathered. On weekends and afternoons in Franklin Park, we climbed a fence surrounding the track and ran. Climbing down, after we ran one day, my foot slipped, striking Joe in the face as I started to fall. He was almost all the way down and caught me somehow as we fell to the ground.

"I'm sorry." I started to cry.

"It's okay," he said. "I'm okay."

I reached out and touched a spot of blood on his lower lip. We stayed on the ground for a minute. I turned on my back but with my head still on his shoulder and looked at the tops of trees above me. "Those trees are very green," I told him, "and the sky is very blue."

"Your eyes are very blue," he said, "but with a little bit of green trim."

I told him my eyes have no green. From the warm, damp ground, I felt winter dissipating.

Then next Sunday, Young Gil was at dinner. Like his dad, he was a tall, lean, light-skinned man, his hair cropped short, a soldier's hair. After dinner, he stayed at the kitchen table, talking with Joe and me as everyone else gathered in other rooms.

"Don't you want to know whether the baby's a boy or a girl?" I asked, turning to him as I dried a plate. Learning the unborn baby's gender was a new option that fascinated me.

"Nah. Of course not. Who wants to know that? The nurse says, *Congratulations, you have a son,* and I say, *Oh yeah, I know.* What fun is that?"

So began a ritual in which Young Gil sat at the table and talked to us while Joe and I did dishes on Sunday. Some evenings, we walked a few blocks to Louise and Young Gil's brownstone for a Scrabble game. Louise never wanted to play Scrabble but puttered around the kitchen while we played. Those were the times I heard him say her Vietnamese name, which sounded like Trang, and sometimes a few words of Vietnamese. I wondered if hearing the language of her country made Louise happy or if it filled her with something like longing for summer in the coldest winter. Louise spoke French, English, and Vietnamese. Usually, when Young Gil spoke Vietnamese, she answered in English. He was the only one she allowed to say her Vietnamese name.

Summer came. Joe got a job running community recreation programs for kids. One night, after he picked me up from my three to eleven janitorial shift, Rosie waited up to greet us on the second floor landing. "I have news." She smiled. "Jacob Gilbert was born a few hours ago. They call him Jake."

Louise came home from the hospital three days later. The next afternoon, a Saturday, Joe and I walked up the street to admire Jake. I offered Louise a box of chocolate, and she thanked me, setting it on a nightstand. "I have to save it for later, in a few months," she explained. "I cannot have it now because it will go into my milk."

Jake lay in a bassinet next to his parents' bed—long, skinny, light-skinned like his father and grandfather—but when I looked into his face, I could see something of the almond shape from his mother's eyes. I couldn't gaze into his eyes for long because he mostly slept. His dad asked us to play Scrabble.

I sat at the kitchen table, eating from a bowl of cherries picked off a tree in the backyard. Young Gil said something in Vietnamese, and Louise answered in the same language this time. Gil explained, "I asked if she remembers how we lost a Monopoly game we had. We lived in this Saigon apartment next to the radio station. Both sides were fighting over the station, but first they fought over our apartment building. They wanted to use it to take the station. We hid under our bed all night."

I was puzzled. "But you were in the crossfire. Didn't the South Vietnamese army guys care that they could accidentally kill you?"

He gave a harsh laugh at my naïveté. "Do you think soldiers care about that in a war? Don't you know anything?"

"Not really."

At the sink, Louise was quiet, her back to us. "Good," her husband said. "I don't want you to know." Just then, Joe racked up forty points with one word, winning the game, while I said a silent thank-you for his high number in the draft lottery.

The next day, sleepy Jake came to Sunday dinner with his parents. After dinner, as Young Gil sat at the table, I asked him if he got very homesick while he was in Vietnam. He thought for a moment. "Not when my wife was there. My home is where she is. My wife is my home."

Summer heat set in. Since birth control pills made me gain weight, I stopped taking them. Those who use the "rhythm" method of contraception are generally known as parents, which is how Joe and I became parents. For the first months of my pregnancy, I threw up, lost weight, and looked like a skinny stick with increasingly large breasts. Fall came. Soda crackers were supposed to help with nausea, and Joe kept a box by our bedside so I could have one first thing each morning. Sometimes, he'd make soup later to go with the crackers.

The highlight of winter was quitting my janitorial job three months before the baby came. Quitting meant I no longer had to wait in the infinite cold for buses that sometimes never came, I no longer had to request larger uniforms each month, and I'd saved enough from my earnings to buy a double bed. I made another change, switching from a clinic on Blue Hill Avenue to a clinic closer to home and affiliated with Beth Israel Hospital, which had a good reputation.

During the last few months of pregnancy, I made up for all the weight I hadn't gained earlier, waddling through the end of another dazed winter into spring, a spring in which I found the challenge of walking even a few blocks exhausting. On the occasions I undertook that challenge, I no longer felt like a glaring white speck in the midst of Roxbury. I felt like a white blimp.

One evening, shortly after my twentieth birthday, I wandered into the kitchen looking for the chocolate cake that Rosie had made. She was sitting at the kitchen table with Young Gil, who had dropped by for a visit. He confessed he'd eaten the last piece. I sat down heavily at the table.

"It doesn't matter," I said, although I was disappointed. "I don't feel so good. I want to eat a whole chocolate cake, but at the same time, I'm getting cramps. It must mean the baby will come tonight. He's a boy, I think."

"Really?" Rosie sounded almost as if my huge pregnancy was a surprise, as if my supposed due date had not passed weeks earlier. She added, "You shouldn't eat anything if you're going into labor."

I nodded, noticing Young Gil's bemused frown in apparent response to more information than he may have wanted about impending birth. I changed the subject, looking at Rosie's short, blue-black hair with its waves and loose curls shining under the kitchen ceiling light. "Your hair is so pretty," I told my mother-in-law.

"Thank you." She smiled. "I've always had good hair. It's the Indian in me. My grandmother's father was an Indian."

"Really? What tribe?"

"I don't know. She never told me."

"Why didn't you ask?"

Rosie sighed. "We didn't want to make the old folks tell us things they didn't want to talk about. We just let them tell us what they wanted to. Her life was hard. During slavery and after. She was a widow with nine children when she came north. She'd buy food for them at Haymarket Square at the end of the day when they marked prices down. She wanted to be a teacher. She didn't get to be, but some of her children and grandchildren did."

I wanted to know more about my baby's great-great-grandmother, but I became preoccupied with pain and waddled off to pace the floors all night, moaning in dramatic martyrdom. In the morning, Joe insisted on taking me to the hospital even though I told him I didn't think the contractions were close enough together yet.

"I do," he said, "and anyway I can't stand you being in this much pain. I'll tell them they have to help you." On our way though, we had to stop near Dudley Street Station for Joe to put gas in the old white Delta 88 Rosie had given us. The muffler had fallen off, so we drove everywhere with the windows open to avoid carbon monoxide poisoning.

At the hospital, a white nurse with brown hair pulled into a bun at the back of her neck told me the baby should come by noon.

"Sooner," I moaned. "Noon is four hours, way too long."

As their shift ended, the white nurse and a black nurse took turns holding my hand. The white nurse told me I'd done a great job, that it wasn't my fault it was taking longer than they'd expected. She had brown eyes that matched her hair.

The black nurse looked about twenty-eight, a little younger than the white nurse, and her eyes were brown too but darker. Her short Afro was only a little longer than Joe's, her skin a little lighter than his. When she held my hand, she looked down into my eyes. "I know you're afraid, but don't be. When I come to work tomorrow, I'll be up to your room to see you and the baby. All this will be over. You'll both be fine." She brushed the hair off my forehead, and in that moment, her hand felt cool against my head so that every part of me didn't hurt quite so much.

As the next shift of nurses came on, Joe took over again, holding my hand, trying to find comforting words, wiping my forehead with a cold cloth. I remember his voice, not his words. I remember sweat shining at the edges of his Afro and on his forehead, his dark eyes with the thick lashes looking down into mine.

Afternoon moves into evening, then night, and what happens next goes something like this. Medical people, nurses, orderlies—I neither know nor care who they are—wheel me into another room. A doctor I haven't seen before comes in, a quiet man with dark blond hair and round wire-rimmed glasses. He and I are alone in the room then. He sits beside me and explains, "The baby's face is looking up at the ceiling instead of down at the floor. It makes everything more difficult, especially with a baby this big. We can't get his head turned, and we can't let this go on."

I don't whisper intentionally. I just can't make my voice any louder when I say, "No kidding—you're telling me?"

The doctor smiles. "We can't let more anesthesia go from your system into the baby's. We have to get him out, either with forceps or a C-section. Forceps are more dangerous. His head could be injured. I want to do the C-section, but I need your permission."

"Where is my husband?"

"I got his permission and sent him downstairs to get some food. He hasn't eaten for a long time, and he's very tired."

"*I'm* very tired," I whisper.

"I know." The doctor pats my hand. "I know you are."

I ask him for a pillow, which he gets. He lifts my head because I can't, and he slips the pillow under it. He sits beside me and smiles a little again. "I'll give you a bikini cut, okay?"

I blink. "A what?"

"A horizontal cut instead of a vertical one so you'll be able to wear a bikini without the scar showing."

"I don't care about that."

"I know, but I'll do it anyway. You might care later. What I'm recommending to you is what I would do for my wife and my baby. Will you let me do it?"

I remember the room as a sea of gleaming whiteness and shining steel. I look at the doctor's white coat. I look up into his eyes. I remember them as gray with flecks of blue and green. I must trust this man, this stranger, to help me now, to know and do the right thing. For an instant, I wonder if the baby and I will live, but then I figure we will.

The doctor watches. "Are we ready to do this?"

"Yes," I say. "You have my permission. Do it."

So they do. ෨

Looking Back

Floyd Skloot

That morning my wife and I felt
summer lose its grip. Nothing more
than a waning of the scents that dwelt
all season near the hilltop, or
softer light, an edge to the breeze
we were not even sure was there.
It was still too early for leaves
to change color, though we saw where
that would begin as we looked back
into the sunlit grove of oak.
When we continued our slow walk
to the crest, neither of us spoke.

℘

Travel of Sound

Nicolas Destino

1. Numbers

In the beginning of his departure from health it would be our hope in medicine. In the beginning of his treatment with medicine it would be our hope in statistics and probability. Statistically speaking, he would have a 70% chance of survival; out of ten chemotherapy medications, seven would not destroy the 100% of his love for combining water and fire to keep people from burning. He would probably consume seven out of ten potato wedges I cooked later one night because three of them would be eliminated by overcooking.

Loss of body mass is the gain of a room's area. He would surrender 25% of his body structure to our house. Distance from the bed to the bathroom would grow. He would plan navigable routes in the house. Objects would become obstacles for the weakened body to walk around, amidst. The house would become an arduous landscape.

55% percent of our friends would ask if Jeffrey was HIV+ because we were each 100% of ourselves. 2% of that 55% would ask twice, even after explanation that he was not. The distance between friendships and foreign objects would diminish. Probability supported that Jeffrey would be respected by nearly everyone who met him. Odds of disrespect would appear as foreign.

A woman appeared, a mother of a friend. She would appear as a foreign object. She would ask if Jeffrey's illness was due to his *lifestyle*. I would say she has a 100% chance of dying. I would tell her that statistically speaking, Jeffrey stands as a small percentage of the United States Air Force, and probability supports that he would eat potatoes, combine water with fire to keep people from burning, and dance happily when eating a good cookie. This would be the style of his life, but this formula would not support the woman's conditions for illness. I make a point to revise her compassion by omitting the period from the end of the sentence

In Jeffrey's presence I would ask nurses questions in ways that might encompass his voice, as he remained conscious and alert but unable to move or speak. The sepsis brought on by chemo complications put him into multi-organ failure, but still the fourteen lines of chemicals would continue to drip inside a body without means of filtration. "How are his liver enzymes? Jeffrey, do you want to hear an update?"

The microwave flashes 12:34 all day and night. A microwave is relatively short: Just millimeters to one meter in length. We're growing in increments. Your kidneys are improving. Your kidneys are flashing 1-2-3-4 all day and night. You have four beats per measure. The quarter note gets the beat. Let's play in 4/4 time. Each kidney is a half note. Remember to talk to them. Imagine light flowing through them. I cannot conduct your kidneys. Did you drink your light today? I have to go home.

Seven people would send healing white light in his direction. Thank you. Very good. Haven't seen light. I am embarrassed. But can't see macrophages either. Understood. Can't see airborne chemicals dispersed or settled in the lungs from Twin Tower debris, but they have inside Jeffrey's. Understood. Human vision is stubborn. Hearing is better. If you lay your ear upon his chest for twenty seconds, walk ten feet away, the memory of heart rate remains for five minutes.

Equal parts light and sound wave mixed into an IV bag. Nurse would tell me the combination appears as whirling phosphorescence and spinning arpeggios. Something trying to escape very fast. Nurse would then tell me her husband is twenty-two years her senior. She is forty. "I married him because I wouldn't have to worry about him chasing a younger number." Understood. There are no equal parts of anything. A part is apart from a part. I would not see the seven parts of sent light. I would hear from seven mouths of seven people: *It's on the way.* I would not see the balance of Nurse's marriage. But I would hear about fidelity, hear about light, hear the memory of heart rate from ten feet away. A partner apart from a partner.

Consequently: Jeffrey becomes part of a ratio. In the way we have two kidneys / one bladder. You / I / are / am. In the language that tries to create the text about one partner to another it is one cigarette / one paragraph. In the language that tries to equate one partner to another as equal parts it is one person / five physicians = one request /one administrative regulation. "May I, unequal part, speak to the intensive physician?" Twenty requests / Twenty rejections. In the language that tries to discern a partner from a monster. Absolutely not.

There are 956 notes in one movement of a particular violin sonata. In 2008 it would be decided that 478 Statue of Libertys' worth of toxic waste can be buried in Erie County, NY. Or it would be settled to only half that amount. I increasingly find myself increasing the divisions. No. Would this happen? Jeffrey, and someone you love, has died. Reader, I would go to fractions over the pieces.

On a morning in Erie County, NY, you would not see toxicity over breakfast. You may go to Roswell Park Cancer Institute for breakfast. Roswell Park Cancer Institute is one of the top cancer research centers in the country or world. To get exact rank you divide the world into countries. A top cancer research center in the most toxic region of a country.

I have to consider the numbers. Beginning with the violin on a morning in Erie County at a top cancer research center, hearing is better so I would play a particular movement of a violin sonata in Jeffrey's IC unit. I would explain to the nurse and Jeffrey: There are 956 notes. That is 956 chances for error. Who can bear this risk? Nurse suggests one note per hour. This would ensure accuracy.

Recovering from sepsis is a slow process. Jeffrey would regulate pulse of various machines, some breathing some beating: beautifully stable metronome. Underground I imagine rows and rows of Statue of Libertys lying on backs, each sealed with care but each a chance for error. Sepsis may occur through intestinal leaks. I wouldn't find it in my hands to play.

"Jeffrey, here is an update": It is today ½ gone on the fifth day of the week. One out of six nurses said she's forgiven us. She has seven letters in her first name. There are three syllables. Soon you will relearn to speak. I don't know why your neck is purple. We're relearning to speak. Syllables come intravenously.

There are 956 syllables in this particular movement of a violin sonata. I would have to begin this movement four times before finding the right voice once. Long ago in a far away position there were 1,365 people watching one violinist. He ended on the open D-string's long tone. The audience walked one-hundred feet and two minutes away. The memory of a ringing D lasted half a year in five-hundred different locations of one country. In the event of an emergency it would take me twenty-two minutes to drive thirteen miles to Roswell Park Cancer Institute. It takes seconds for the ringing D to get there.

Beginning a fourth time to the completion of 956 syllables of music: I would look at his immobile and voiceless body in a room of sound and motion. Each tone sounds at a different frequency. Each tone travels at a different speed. This cubic den of recovery/ decay would contain immobility against travel of sound. Every note trying to escape very fast. I have to go home.

2. Pre positions & Possessives

The pre position is that it was your body. The pre position is that it was your voice. As a child you were taught to use your body and your voice toward the creation of language. In the beginning of mapping the environment through your body and voice, toward the creation of language with sounds and motions, you were told: this is good. Because you have this tissue and nerve den that is all you really own. That is all.

With stands as a central preposition. You will take your den with you to every arrival. Go to the grocery store with your body.

Just try to leave it home. With you is you. Go to the concert hall. With you is you, your own arrival and departure. The pre position is that it was your body occasionally leased by others. After the loss of your voice or motion is removal of language. Ownership expires.

Shifting is an exercise practiced by violinists to learn to move smoothly from one position into another. The smoother one shifts, the more accurate the pitch and tempo. Be prepared for what follows. Maintain control over your bow. Elbow, wrist, fingers flexing toward coordination. Maintain the balance points and equal weight distribution of the bow from frog to tip.

In 1839 there was a violinist whose musical voice was celebrated throughout Venice. He was known as a vocalist. The sweetness of his violin carried like the human voice. His fine muscle dexterity translated into crystal clearness in fast passages. But when the cadenza approached, he temporarily lost flexibility in his fingers and wrist. He lost tempo and pitch. Things fell apart. He was booed off the stage.

The pre position is that it was his body and his voice. In practicing, he learned to use his body and voice toward the creation of language, vio-linguistically. Being booed off the stage was a rejection of an entire body because it fell apart. He has not been forgiven. Many years later I find myself agitatedly stalled behind an elderly pedestrian. I am trying to forgive myself for the loss of motion in her body.

Forget illness. Illness is out of fashion. It's only fashionable to be slightly late to the party. Illness deducts speed. You're not invited. Sick people don't dance. They don't tell jokes. They don't have sex! It's best to start speaking of a sick person in the past tense because they don't move and shake, but crawl and tremble. I wonder about our intolerance of slow motion.

Anywhere in the world, any number of thousands of years into history, where the first sadness occurred when the human body's limitations were revealed; no one knows. Was it the inability to keep up with horses? The inability to escape from a running lion or swimming shark? The envy of speed and efficiency resulted in wheels. The rolling of wheels resulted in the hitching of humans to horses. Today in a fire station they are taking thirty-minute breaks for the chance to slow their motions, relax. Terminally ill people are too dissimilar from motion. Jeffrey wouldn't shift smoothly from rescue worker to patient. We have to shift somewhere illogical to fetch the condition.

Into is an intimate preposition. You grow into another person as another person grows into you. Into is a total absorption. In the beginning of your partner's departure from health you may also shift into a new position. But what? When a concourse of parts falls apart, then what? You can't really divide a human body then call it a body. It is fractioned into malfunctions. The total absorption into loss. Lose your voice. Someone will speak for you. Shifting is an exercise practiced by violinists to learn to move smoothly from one position into another. Into is an intimate preposition, and I would also lose my voice into Jeffrey's silence.

Challenge: Shift love into pornography. Holding Jeffrey's hand and kissing his forehead would begin to feel like pornography in the presence of others: one/one + lips + forehead = comfort + discomfort. You would not have to ask this for me to tell you. There is an anxiety of shifting between two dimensions. The pre position is that it was terribly silent. The post position is that it was terribly silent. Jeffrey would come home from reserves into himself and into ourselves. Shifting is tricky. Lose your voice. Someone will speak for you.

Before and during, I wouldn't realize the wrenching of *after* until an aftermath. Now. Or an after calculation of numbers. When I would try to recount the previous day's heart rate but found interruptions by new and unevenly shifted positions of data, then what? Now entering the after with and into the departure from sounds. Now, the music of machinery, and I would see light sent out in digital numerology. In 2009 you might hear Vivaldi's music and wonder if he knows what happened after himself:

Now. After. After what? After you were born. After you were born, then what? After you were born and then luminous. After you were born and then luminous what? After you were born and then. After you were born. After you were. After you. After. "He's in a better place." Now. No! Human vision is stubborn. If you want before, during, and after in one field of vision, then you have to go to a better place before you can speak of it. I have to go home.

I take my body to a car I bought with loaned money. Having borrowed New York State's toll road, anything could happen in the twenty-two minutes it takes to get home from Roswell Cancer Institute. Sometimes I may want to feel thankful for loaned lights on thruways. The sun: Sometimes I may feel thankful for the sun because I can say it is mine—in that it belongs to no one in particular. Driving into orange light—it is mine: total absorption— away from an orange-tinted Jeffrey whose liver is on loan for observation by physicians at Roswell Park, whose body was never mine or anyone else's. I may want to become possessive: of the numbers, of the data, of the concourse of malfunctioned parts simplified as his 'body.' &

Something Happened

Tim Nolan

When he almost died that night—
under the glaring hospital lights—

she stood off in the corner—she was
herself—she would have been fine

if he died that night—we were all
ready for it to happen—then—it didn't—

And he came back to himself—not
remembering anything about his

struggles—they happened in a dream—
She—could not stand the up and down of it—

Something happened—*can we say this?*—
something happened—when he came back.

ॐ

Intensive Care Unit

Tim Nolan

The *Intensivist* has told us
about the heart the lungs
the kidneys—how they are all

Failing—despite the multiple drips
of drugs from the blinking
IV machines—he's on a machine

Called *Arctic Sun*—that cools
him down—to give him a chance
to heal himself—In the Arctic—

Fishermen fall in the deep
cold and come back later
around the blazing fire—

Later—when they warm him up—
a flush comes back to his cheeks—
vivid purple bruises up and down

His arms—his arms like fried chicken
wings—his tender flanks—the bunched-
up hospital gown—we cover him up—

Not for modesty's sake—
but to keep him warm—in this strange
Arctic light—his cold clear breath—

∞

Poem in Which I Pack You a Few Things for the Hospital

Beverley Bie Brahic

"Stop wasting electricity"

What if you catch me—if you
lift the latch with a ghostly click
and find me ruffling your soft things?
Undies, silky white on the right,
left, lacy black. Socks, six pair, filed
according to color: like Mendel
discovering the filiation of peas.
And here is your nightie: better
than the uniform hospital gown.
I lay it in the vanity case.

In the laundry room—smoothed into squares—
frayed diapers you still employ
to dust surfaces of nesting tables
and the helpless bric-a-brac gods:

I weep with the sound off as I was taught,
mustn't disturb others with your pain.

Promise I'm not snooping—I unearth the tin
of shortbread, with fluted edges.
I snitch two cookies. You won't mind
if I drink your scotch.
I pull a few books off your shelf;
one marble flyleaf is inscribed
Audrey P—, Saskatchewan, 1938:
Tennyson's *Complete Works.*

Doubt you'll miss it. One quick phone call.
At the ER you insisted:
Use the phone as much as you like,
then, fast, words spilling like dice
from a hand unexpectedly opened—
I'm sure glad you've come. Years
since I said my prayers, kneeling
at the bedside as I was taught—

what are these words that stumble unasked
to stammer at the knees of speech—

hush child—go to bed try to sleep.

&

Crazyland

Ruth Schemmel

"My two girls are home!" my mother exclaimed, shuffling across the linoleum to give my sister Celeste and me big showy kisses. *Mmmmmhaah.* I wriggled out of her embrace as quickly as politeness allowed, handing her my six-month-old baby in the car seat as a diversion, a kind of baby shield. My mother had taken hands-off parenting to literal extremes. She had plenty of reasons for it, if you wanted to dig into her past, but it didn't make her late-onset physicality any easier to stomach. Now that Celeste and I were adults she wanted to pretend she had been a different kind of parent, all along, and we were different kinds of kids.

"Traffic around the airport was a nightmare," Celeste said, dropping her keys on the kitchen table with a thud. "We had to wait an hour for June's bags and the baby's car seat."

I relaxed, watching her redraw the lines, establish the old roles. The big sister, forever put out and burdened by me. At least I no longer threatened to outshine her, now that she had established herself as a lawyer—a bare-knuckled public defender, but a lawyer all the same—while I had shelved plans of graduate school in literature for part-time remedial teaching and a paycheck. Such as it was.

"Those highways." My mother shook her head. "I don't know how anyone drives on them." My mother's hair had its usual choppy look. She must have been cutting it herself again, probably while watching TV and drinking sherry, with whatever scissors she found lying around. Sewing scissors, maybe, or one for nails. Celeste had tried to improve my mother's appearance when my mother ran away from Dad last spring, but whatever style lessons Celeste had given her had not taken root. The Old Girl, as Celeste liked to call her, was walking around in stretch-waisted flex pants that bagged around her knees and exposed inches of blue-veined ankle. She wore a voluminous blue T-shirt, too—"Come and get it!"—which she'd gotten free with mailed-in dog food labels, if I know my mother. She looked thinner than ever, her skin slack from weight loss. Celeste had a theory that when Mom ran off she was shucking Dad for good, getting ready for a new life without him, but you could not look at her face now and believe it. She had the wild, vacant look of a last survivor, her gaze fixed on Celeste and me as if she could not let us out of her sight.

My father was dying of cancer—we had known this for five years—but in the last several months he had developed dementia to boot. It was scary dementia—paranoid, unpredictable—not the gentle forgetting, the peeling away of years, names, faces. The night my mother left him, he had called the police while she was sleeping to have her taken away, convinced she was the crazy one. "You don't need to take me," she told the responding officer, a shy man scarcely out of his teens. "I'll just go." Her flight from Dad lasted only a week, before guilt called her back. Now three months later he'd had a flight of his own—in the car, by himself, in his bathrobe. He had been found in the parking lot of a JC Penney across the state and was now waiting at the hospital where they had taken him to be picked up.

Celeste had been first to notice the dementia. She had been quick to decipher my mother's cryptic, unhelpful communiqués; she read between the lines of my mother's terse postcards, made the connections even my mother had missed, noted inconsistencies, the eventual, final stretching of my father's lifelong eccentricity into insanity. The long foretold craziness had at last arrived! (For certainly it had been foretold; certainly we had long seen it coming, since our earliest run-ins with parental unreason.) Our parents were crazy! One of them, anyway. One for now. We had long phone conversations, poring over evidence, recounting each crazy story, each detail.

You could say it brought us together.

What we didn't do—what didn't happen—was we didn't fly out to Virginia from our respective cities—Celeste from Philadelphia (think *Rocky* or cheese steak); me from Seattle (think matcha green tea)—to be with my mom and help her decide things. Not until now.

When I got the call that my father was missing, I made day-care arrangements for my three-year-old and left her with my husband, Miles, planned a week of lessons for the substitute who would teach my "second chance" class of high-school dropouts, and with my six-month-old baby Livvie in tow, flew from Seattle to the family house in Virginia. Celeste, not to be outdone, rushed home, too, beating me by a good two hours. So there we were, facing things like a family.

You may say finally. You may say that.

My mother invited us to sit and poured us bowls of a "traveler's soup" she had made for the occasion of our visits. "This is what I do when people come over," she said, as if people came over all the time.

"Hey, where's the old table?" I asked, missing the solid, warm-colored oak, one of the few quality purchases from my parents' garage-sale forays. It was far nicer than the shabby white Formica in its place.

"Your sister took that one," my mother said, with an indulgent smile.

"What?" Celeste snapped at me, before I could say anything. "I needed a table."

"She cleaned us out on her last visit," my mother said, with a patient, amused look.

Celeste laughed, as if it were pert and gutsy of her to rob my father of one of the last few items of quality he would have in his life. He would never have another kitchen table. There were no kitchen tables in his future. Just the white Formica.

"I don't want to eat at this junky table," I said.

"Well, it's all about what June wants," said Celeste.

I decided to ignore this. "Good soup, Mom," I said.

"Is it? I think it's awful. I ruined it with salt. You don't find it too salty?"

"Jesus," Celeste broke in, rolling her eyes. "Can you take a compliment without rubbing your own nose in it?"

"Nice image, Celeste," I said, in an earnest, faux-admiring way. I had developed this persona—the goofy, gullible professorial type, with no ability to perceive sarcasm—especially for Celeste, so as not to threaten her with my supposed intelligence. Or maybe she had developed the persona for me. Who could tell anymore? The act got its usual laugh.

"Well, you're the cook of the family, June," my mother told me. This was shaky ground if not complete fiction. Yes, I could cook, but only if I followed the recipe slavishly. I was a cook compared to Celeste, whose idea of cooking was setting the microwave on high. This, in my family, was how legends started, the kind that simmered on back burners for years, seasoned with resentment, salted with hate: my mother heaping undeserved praise on one of us, as if to make up for that lifetime of hands-off parenting verging on neglect. In twenty years Celeste would probably announce that she was opening a chain of restaurants. She would show me, show us all. See? She was always the cook!

"Cooking is a waste of time," Celeste said now, dismissively.

Pleasantries thus out of the way, we began to work out our plan, which was more like an expression of hope. Hope—the thing with feathers. The thing had a beak, too, and talons, if not outright claws, but for the moment I was focused on the hope.

"Maybe Dad can stay at the hospital where he is now," I suggested.

"They won't let him," my mother said. "They were very clear about that on the phone."

"Who was clear about it?" Celeste asked. The public defender. "Who did you talk to?"

"A person. Just some person. The person from the hospital. They were very clear about—"

"A person from the hospital? Mom, you need to ask for names," Celeste said with the beginnings of anger. I knew we were in trouble. If we could not agree now, there was no way we could put my father someplace safe, in a hospital, where he could stay, which was beginning to seem like the best chance of saving him. Saving all of us.

The next morning—a hot summer day, a scorcher, my dad would say—we drove to get him, my sister riding shotgun, the baby in the back by my mother, who cooed at her and grabbed her toes. We were punchy, lighthearted, as we drove through bright cornfields and pastures of stolid cows, but conversation dropped off as we approached the hospital, stuck in the middle of what appeared to be nowhere. The kind of nowhere my sister and I had lost no time leaving. The kind we left our parents behind to grow old in. Happily ever after. Think of that.

The hospital was beige brick, squat and square, with green windows that made me think of Legos. The whole thing could have been designed by a child: obvious corners, right angles, those green translucent slabs of glass. It looked like a strip mall office complex, or the headquarters of an online university, with a few show-box, street-level classrooms. Inside, these impressions did not last long. You noticed the wheelchair ramps and disinfectant, the safety glass and occasional man or woman in a white coat.

I saw my father a second before he noticed me, before the door opened and they led him to the industrial-gray-carpeted waiting room. I was shocked at how shrunken he looked. He had always been short, and a little stout. Now he looked starved, consumed. Someone had shaved off his beard, and his chin, exposed, was small and mean looking. I had not exactly forgotten he had cancer, but it was the first time I saw its impact on his body, and I remembered he was dying.

"Dad! So good to see you!" I said as brightly as I could. I set down the baby on the floor and hugged him. Moving with geologic slowness, he turned to watch Livvie as she did her lopsided crawl across the carpet, rolling onto one hip, a plump leg curling behind her.

"See you later, alligator," he said to her, tongue fumbling the Ls, and then he waited, as if Livvie could reply. I realized he was confusing her with my three-year-old, with whom he had had that conversation. He started, with massive slowness, to bend over, so he could hear.

"What are you doing, Thomas?" one of the two harried-looking aides at his side chided, voice sharp with recrimination, maybe fear. Did she think he would hurt the baby? The aides both lunged at him, half dragging him to the couch, while signaling me to get the baby out of the way.

"Call the police," my father said, his voice a growl.

"Thomas has not been very nice this morning," one of the aides said.

Are you kidding me? This is a joke, right? I waited for Celeste to say. The man is dying. He has dementia. He is not a child.

But Celeste was silent. We all were.

A petite middle-aged woman in a robin's-egg-blue suit came in and slid her arm through my mother's, as if they were the best of friends. "Let's have a chat," she said, pointing her chin towards an office.

"Mom, do you want one of us to come with you?" I said.

"We'll all have a chance to chat," the woman assured me. "Now, which one of y'all's the lawyer?"

Celeste followed her out of the room, wearing what I supposed was her courtroom face: eyes wide and pleased looking, eyebrows slightly lifted, as if she were heading off for an interesting discussion. We were all pretending something. Only my father had an expression appropriate to the horror of the occasion. Maybe that was what madness was—the inability to play along.

When Celeste and my mother returned, I had my own moment to speak with the woman, whoever she was. Office manager? Social worker? I could not say. Her role, as far as I could tell, was to get my dad out of that hospital. Although I raised every question and objection I could think of, nothing could change the facts, which she laid out for me like bricks, one by one, paving me into a wall. The hospital could do nothing for him: no mental evaluation, no diagnosis of any kind, not even a take-home packet of drugs, for when the heavy antipsychotics they had given him wore off. We had two choices: take the man home, or trick him into an ER at a hospital that had a mental health facility, and leave him: a forced commitment. But home we could not manage. Home would require Celeste or me to be there. To live there, to help. And that, we both knew, would not happen.

"The second one," I said. "That's what we'll do, the second option."

"It's Dad's house," Celeste said. "How can we tell him he can't go back to his own house? I don't like it, June."

"Whatever you girls think," said my mother, wan and passive as a kindergartner on a field trip.

"Celeste, we can't," I said.

My mother shrugged, picked up a pen, and signed the papers. Then my father was ours again, ours to keep, such as he was. All sales final, no returns.

"Now can we finally go home?" my father said, as we walked him to the hot parking lot.

"Are you hungry, Dad?" I asked. "We were thinking we might stop for lunch." Actually, we were thinking we might stop somewhere so that we could call the Richmond hospital for directions. But I kept this to myself.

"Fine. Just—bring me home."

Celeste stared at me. My mother gazed out at the empty sky.

When my mother left my father alone last spring, I called my father every day from my apartment in Seattle. It took seven or eight rings for him to pick up, seven or eight rings during which I pictured him traipsing through the fields in his bathrobe, pursued by terrors, fleeing demons. I saw him perched on the roof, the house in flames. I imagined him taking flight, like the various madwomen breaking free from their attics in the nineteenth-century novels I had read and reread in college until the bindings broke. Or just drifting, ghost-like, through the cluttered rooms. Was he shouting? Crying? Praying? He had a dog with him, a dog he loved. I wondered if he would remember to feed her. Then he picked up the phone, and I knew that he was safe. His voice came through the receiver, warm, reassuring, the voice I knew, but it also sounded care-worn and sad, as I asked him how he was, if he was eating and whether he had seen *Jeopardy,* his favorite television show, the night before. He was so worried about Mom, he would say, and then the madness would creep into his voice, as he accused her of sabotaging his computer, or secretly provoking the dog to pee inside the house—things I knew my mother had never done. "She's sick! Sick!" he said.

My mother came home, the Old Girl did. Things were not right—things would never be right—but she was there. "We're in Crazyland," she said in an odd voice when I asked her how things were. I heard his voice in the background and winced to think he was in the room when she said that. Fearing what he believed was my mother's craziness, my father had buried the guns in the fields before she returned home. That detail got me: the guns we had always heard about and hardly ever seen—the guns he had bought to protect us from intruders—buried. The logic frightened me, the care and love and loneliness. The truth was intruders had sacked the fortress, broken the windows, stolen the jewels, stolen my father's mind. Intruders had their run of the place. Old man. Old man. I could imagine him out in the field, with his shovel.

"What's going on?" my father demanded now, taking a few jerky, vigorous steps and stopping. It was four in the afternoon; we had just parked on the top ramp of the hospital garage, the only open space. The place was packed with emergencies. Celeste looked like an emergency, for one, her face red with summer heat, her eyes snapping with barely contained rage. Her expression was a lot like our Dad's, actually. Both of them glowered at me. My mother stood there, smiling weakly, arms hanging limp.

"The baby's sick," I said lightly. Easily.

"The baby?" he said.

"Sick."

He looked at the hot weight on my shoulder, Livvie's body dense with sleep. He nodded and looked away, his expression shifting to concern, and maybe shame, for thinking about himself rather than the sick baby. The Virginia gentleman. The truly gentle man, the grandfather. Even now.

I was beginning to feel sick myself, about what I was doing, what I was going to do.

As we walked toward the entrance, my mother hung back, holding my father's arm solicitously, while Celeste pushed ahead, nodding for me to keep up with her.

"That was awful," she whispered. "When you kept stopping the car and turning around? Getting lost? He was freaking out. He knew something was up."

"Really?"

"I don't know about this," she said.

I was thinking: will he stop? Will he look up at the word "Emergency" and realize he is having one? Will he run, fight us? Will this get physical? Or will he keep going, head straight into the hospital, maybe knowing—*knowing* what we are doing to him, but going in anyway, out of love?

Inside, a man at the intake desk asked about the nature of our emergency. My mother and father were walking behind me, not yet through the door, not yet in earshot. "It's my father. Dementia," I said. "He doesn't know that's why we're here. He thinks there's a problem with my baby."

The man put down his pen and looked at me, eyes black and steady. *Are you kidding me?* he might have been thinking. Or maybe: *Don't do this.* More likely he was thinking: *When's this goddamned shift over?*

I held his gaze. Think what you want. Judge if you want. Throw rocks, if you must. Just do this for me now.

He picked up his pen and began writing. "Patient's name?" he asked, his face blank, not judging. Not visibly. And that was fine. These people were professionals. I could count on that, after all. And I was almost done.

Now my mother and father stood behind us in the lobby, but my father was too busy looking around, too dazed and overwhelmed to catch that I was giving his vitals to the desk clerk.

He sidled over to me. "So, is the baby all right?" He looked anxious. Normal.

"She's fine," I said, shifting Livvie from one arm to the other, trying to make my voice warm and reassuring. "Dad—"

"Mr. Griffin? Thomas?" A woman in a white coat—a nurse or an orderly—took him by the elbow. "Please come with me. I need to ask you some questions." She bent her head engagingly to the side, with a smile that did not reach her eyes. A man stood behind her, a big man. He was smiling, too.

My father turned to me and gave me a look. He stood there for what felt like fifteen minutes but could only have been a second or two and treated me to that look, which if you have seen it, and maybe you have, you know is the worst kind of stare a parent can give you, because it reminds you of the lifetime of sacrifices that parent has made for you, which you have thrown away like trash. Is it possible for this look to have the same effect if delivered by someone other than the parent who raised and gave up everything for you, who drove away from the home he saved for so he could sit behind a desk in an office through your diaper years and preschool and gawky adolescence, missing almost everything, mostly for the house he provided, the decaying wonder which he now wants nothing more than to return to, to die in?

Maybe. We would have to ask Judas Iscariot, or perhaps Brutus. Maybe one day, while I am rotting in hell, or burning, or whatever activities are planned there—while I am replaying this exact moment over and over, for eternity, as a gristle-flecked eagle pecks out my liver, for example—I will.

"Dad, we want to get you help," I said. I still smiled the fake smile, the helpful, attentive expression. I felt the room closing in on me; as if it were a dream, as if this were happening inside my head, as if my head were a submerged island, which I suppose is not an island any more, not if it's submerged, but rather the tip of an undersea mountain, and looking up I could see a faint light, which might have been the world, and each word was a message for that world, an attempt to reach and reclaim it, except that they were empty words, just bubbles of air.

"Well, thanks a lot," he growled, in his so-you-want-to-be-a-wise-guy voice, as if I had given him a tuna sandwich when he specifically asked for ham.

I watched them lead him away. And thought: almost free.

My mother went to the office to complete more paperwork, which took most of the next three hours. It is not easy to divest a man of his rights to everything—to life, liberty—which was probably a good thing. Celeste and I sat together in vinyl bucket seats, and Livvie, now in her quiet awake state, sat on my lap and looked around calmly. A scattering of people sat propped in chairs as if they had washed up there, expressions of pain or trauma or regret etched in their faces.

"That was awful," Celeste said again. "You have no idea."

Just then I glanced up and saw Dad heading for the exit. He looked like a man with a purpose, a man with intentions; so sure of himself that, even though he was wearing a hospital gown, even though he had been checked in—against his will, a psychiatric emergency—no one gave him a second glance.

"That was Dad," I said.

"Shit," Celeste said.

With Livvie in my arms, I ran to the intake nurse, the man who had looked at me so intently when I came in. "That was my father," I said. "He just walked out."

The man sprang into action, darting forward, delivering orders to two aides. Within seconds they led Dad back. He looked like a mental patient suddenly, defeated in his gown and slippers. He must have hated that it took three of them to walk him back, one on each arm and another in front of him, talking to him in a calm quiet voice.

"This is a mistake!" Dad kept saying, sounding harried, but also like he did not quite believe the situation, as if he knew the evidence was mounting against him. He did not meet my eyes as he passed by, inches away.

When I slunk back to my seat, Celeste and I exchanged *oh-shit* looks—eyebrows raised as if to say: could this get any more terrible?—and suddenly both of us teetered into hilarity. I slapped my hand over my mouth to keep bubbles of laughter from escaping. We could not look at each other. Think of sad things, I told myself. Think of *other* sad things. There was a hurricane somewhere, homes destroyed. Think of that.

Celeste made a clicking sound; I risked a glance and saw she was barely holding it together; laughter threatening to spill out. She caught my gaze, which set us both off.

A woman in the waiting room eyed me angrily—a woman with her own emergency—and my eyes slid past her.

"Dad's escape," I gasped, and Celeste and I both laughed, eyes squeezed shut, squeezing out tears, not daring to look at each other.

A nurse came through the flap doors, looked around, and walked over to me. "You're June? Your father wants to see you."

This sobered me up. Celeste too. I traded glances with her, which the nurse caught.

"Are you going to go see him?" the nurse asked. No right or wrong. No correct response.

"Yes, I'll go," I said. Burning with shame.

I gave Livvie to Celeste and followed the man through the flap doors to a triage area, where my father lay—docile, sedated—on a cot, the sheets pulled up to his chest, an IV drip in his arm and two nurses standing on either side of him.

"Let me talk to my daughter alone," he said to them, no longer demanding, but requesting; the tired patriarch. Grant me this reasonable request. Me, a dying man.

They looked at me. He did not seem capable of springing up again, of fleeing; of grabbing me as a human shield; of brandishing a sudden knife—although part of me wished that he could; part of me wanted to see that happen. Part of me wanted him to break out, break free, take off; a sick man in flight—except that I knew he could never be free.

"Hi Dad," I said, once the nurses had left.

"Look, I forgive you," he said. Wasting no time. Time, he did not have. He knew this. "I know you had to do that, with the baby. I know they made you."

Made me? I could not answer.

"Listen, you're my only chance. You're the only one, June. You've got to tell them about your mother."

"Mom?"

"You've got to tell them she's sick. She needs to get help. You've got to tell them she's the crazy one." He looked at my face, his voice a conspiratorial whisper. I could not speak. "All those things I told you about her," he said.

I thought back to our phone conversations, when my mother was gone and he was alone, how I had listened to him, and how he had taken my silence for agreement.

"Dad," I said carefully. "I think you need help. I think they can help you here."

He looked at me blankly. "Well, that's it. I'm dead. My life is over. I see that now."

"Dad—I—"

"You can go," he said, his voice hardening, anger deepening the lines in his face. "Go now. Go home. I'm dead."

I started to leave.

"Send in your sister," he growled.

Back in the waiting area, Celeste slumped in the seat, the baby in her arms, the hilarity that had gripped her gone. "Well?" she said.

"He wants to see you."

She nodded. I took Livvie from her, and she trudged to the flap doors and disappeared. A few minutes later she was back, her face grim. We sat and did not speak.

After a while my mother joined us. Paperwork finished. "That's it. We're done," she said. It had taken hours, maybe; I had lost track of time. "We're free," my mom went on. She smiled at us with uncertainty. "We can go."

We started to walk out. "You really did it," my mother said to me. "You stayed strong. Otherwise we would have taken him home."

"Yeah, you were the one," Celeste said, grudgingly.

I tried to think of a reply to that.

"I couldn't have handled him alone," my mother gushed, as we entered the parking lot. It was late by then—after ten at night. We were on the top floor of a parking garage, the roof. Searing lights blocked any view of stars or moon. The breeze on my skin was delicious, mild and cool.

No, she could not have handled him alone. Not alone. In different families, there might be other ways to handle this. Different wives might have handled it another way, and different kids might have come home to live with their parents. Taken leave from work. Helped out. Other people knew how to manage things like this, this incident with my father. Other people did things the right way, appropriately. Other people did not laugh hysterically while committing their father to a mental hospital when he was dying of cancer, for example. But those other people were not here, and we were it, the only people my father had.

Celeste left the next day; she had cases to attend to, trials pending. I stayed a few more days. I visited my father in the hospital. There were no more scenes; no more attempted escapes. His doctors experimented with dosages, prescriptions, although they made no pretense at hope. My father secured extra slipper socks, the kind that turn to paper when you wash them. "Give these to Miles," my father said. "I've got a connection here."

He's adjusting, I thought, but when my mom looked away, he mouthed to me, "Call the police. They'll get me out of here."

Back in my Seattle apartment, I shuffled things around on my syllabus. I changed the font on my resume, played with margins, made it new and sent it around. On weekends Miles and the kids and I drove around aimlessly and looked at houses from internet real estate sites, houses we might buy someday, if I got a better job, if we earned a little more. We drove through wooded suburbs named for fantastical sounding forests. We stopped at every "for sale" sign, gazed at empty windows.

From afar, I monitored my father. I called him nights after I knew he'd finished watching *Jeopardy*. Sometimes I sat on hold for ten minutes, fifteen. Sometimes the staff did not know who Thomas Griffin was. Sometimes they had never heard of him. In the minutes of waiting, I imagined he had gotten out. Broken free. I could feel the fabric of the hospital gown, a light weight on his shoulders, the asphalt and gravel through his hospital bed socks as he ran—sure, let him run—more of a hobble, really, but motion, the night air cool on his face and arms. I could feel his lungs pulling for one breath, and another, the moon bright overhead, a lure, like the promise you meant when you made it. ဢ

As Broken in the End

Travis Mossotti

It wasn't June but late August when
my father slowed the minivan

onto the shoulder—a sign: *Hot
Boiled Peanuts*, a white paper bag

turning translucent with grease,
oil cooling on the steering wheel.

What brand of wisdom does one buy
from a roadside stand swaddled

in Spanish moss at the tail end
of a Floridian summer on the last

family vacation? Not a single word
was ever spoken about what it meant

to quietly raise a family, to suffer
as his father suffered, to be a man.

&

Family Waiting Room
Intensive Care Unit

Stacy Nigliazzo

1. *5 a.m.*

I feel the sharp
sting

of silver thistles in
my hair,

asleep this night
in a hardback

chair cut
from particle board and plastic.

2. *Pancytopenia*

I dream of her fair
skin bled

purple and blue like
blackberries

settled in a cream pot.

3. *Eucharist*

I awake,
teeth pooling, red—then

spit them out—
grasping white shadows

on the cold ceramic floor.

4. *Drape*

The latch, unhitched—
my legs, not

yet awake—riddled with pins,
carry me

through the parting
steel door.

&

Odd a Sea's Wake

Nicholas Patrick Martin

I don't want him to die. You think this a lot. All the time. Nonstop. It etches into you until the groove is so deep the blade can't escape. And deeper still. This thought more than any other becomes a part of you. Something unwanted. Like a parasite. You can't burn it off or cut it out or kill it with medicine. This recurring thought. This broken record. This song you can't get out of your head. It's more true than anything you thought you were capable of ascribing degrees of truth to. Grammar doesn't apply here. It's crude and vague. What does it mean for something to be true. You love this man. You didn't at first. That took years. You were friends who became lovers who stayed friends. And now he's leaving you. You don't want him to die. The truth of this thought that seems to actually have mass and weight inside you is more true than you thought possible. It's an immaculate truth. A truth so inviolate and profound and basically true that you don't know how to interpret it exactly. It's almost too much to handle. Because it's true. And it's true also that this truth that you've decided is more true than any other truth you've ever encountered could die with him. This truth will expire with him if he dies. If you don't want him to die and he dies you'll sound pretty silly saying you don't want him to die. People will think you're whacko. You'll accidentally let it slip that you don't want him to die and guess what they'll say. He *is* dead. Maybe you need some help. We know this must be rough for you. Time heals all wounds and all that. And you'll say go fuck yourself. Don't even start with me you'll say and then get very angry. Because who are they after all. They're not him is who they are. They're everybody you don't want them to be. They're people who could never understand. And this renders them useless.

You don't say this of course. That you don't want him to die. This heartbreaking pearl of truth you keep to yourself. Locked safely away in your mind where it accretes and expands. Only not smooth. You discover this truth is jagged and only gets worse. Look at his face while he sleeps. Watch his labored breathing. The little twitches and half-utterances that describe the tender unseen moments in which a lifetime of private anguish resides. Not his but yours. Yours because it's his. He stirs and reaches for you in a half-sleep and you cry. Of course you cry. What else can you do. Cover his naked body. So frail. Maybe a nightmare. He's visibly upset. Jerks and mumbles inaudible syllables you desperately try to decipher. Search for something you know isn't there. It's just a dream. It's not him. It's his brain. You learn to distinguish between the two. He confronts something in this dream and shakes violently. You stroke his hand and coo to him but let the nightmare take its course. You remember reading somewhere it's better to let them work through it. So much of what you know are these vestiges of accumulated information. The origins of which you'd never be able to pinpoint. But they stuck and so you incorporate them into this discouraging farce that isn't really. It's much worse. But you try to be big about it. Be reasonable. Rational in other words. Objective. Which is a joke. There's nothing objective about watching someone you love wither away and die. You can't read it in a book and know. Can't know until it happens to you and even then you still can't know. It's the not knowing that kills you both.

His eyelids flutter and you see the whites of his eyes. This part is called the sclera. You don't know how you know this. But you hate it. When his eyes do this and it looks like nobody's home. Like he's just a brain and not him. This man you love. This man whose laugh is reason enough. Whose body you know like your own imperfections. You feel like a cartographer of old joys and more recent sufferings. Moles and birthmarks and odd bends in anatomy. Wrinkles and liver spots and now blisters. Bed sores. These you develop a special hatred for. There's simply no need for it. There's something reprehensible about their very existence. Their presence on his body. You think on top of everything he needs this. These sores that require constant cleaning and care. As if his sickness wasn't enough. As if his sickness. Wasn't. Enough.

You curse them and he asks what's the matter and you get angry. Tell him to shut up and keep still. You want to give up. Other truths are evinced. Truths you don't want to acknowledge. That these sores will never heal. That you'll be doing this until the day he dies. You ask yourself what's the point. And then he winces in pain. That expression when you've been too rough and it breaks your heart. He winces like that and you say you're sorry and he tries to smile for you. Because he is a better person. Because he is the one who's sick and here he doesn't want to hurt your feelings. You are worthless. You are a horrible person. This isn't his fault. And here you complain. Look at his ass. His back. Open and raw and spilling foulness onto the bed. He lays in this. Sleeps in this. Wakes to this. He's in constant pain. He has a tube inserted into his penis. And you complain. You secretly say terrible things. You call him names. And he winces in pain and you're suddenly made aware of what a despicable person you are. How craven and insensitive and mean. Look at him and say it to his face. Tell him what you mutter under your breath when he falls asleep. Fall asleep crying in a chair next to his bed.

Hold the spoon over a cupped hand and let him have a taste. He smiles and goes back to his magazine. Not quite there yet you say. Bring him the cutting board on a tray he can place on his lap. It's easier for him this way. Doesn't have to worry if he spills. He likes green peppers the best. He doesn't know why. He thinks maybe it's because they're hollow. He chops and chops and chops. He'd get embarrassed and then angry if you told him the truth. That you thought it was sweet how he likes to help. Not too small you tell him. But not too big either. You see a look of ordinary frustration on his face and you're blindsided by the most delightful and ineffable joy. A word he despises. Ineffable not joy. Why. Because it isn't the sickness. It isn't the pain he's upset with. It's the boring old you. Think never again will I take for granted the little quotidian snags of life. They are gifts. Well which is it. How big do you want these damn peppers. You smile and he says what and you go nothing. Why don't you tell him. You don't know the answer to that either.

You confuse love with indignation and indignation with enthusiasm. Bitch all you want he says. Wasting your time. You know deep down that he's right. But you want to prove it to him. And this is where the confusion manifests itself. You pretend to be tough. You're going to kick ass and take names. He'll see. Your anger will be a vessel incapable of containing your love. Unveil your pissed-off face and go to work. This is absurd but you feel the need to proclaim it. Smash fists on countertops and argue with him when he tells you to give it up. But you can't. This you tell him is impossible. You'll prove it. That you love him and feel sick with rage and genuine indignation that something like this could happen. Illustrate your devotion through exhaustive acts of pointlessness. Refuse to let it go. Assure him that they're not going to get away with this. He shrugs and you sort of want to join him. Because he's right. They already have. Write a thousand letters. Clang a cup forever and ever and it'll never make one bit of difference.

Wake up and go through your routine. You've always gotten ready first. He doesn't like it when you're gone for long stretches of time. He gets anxious. Scared. He doesn't even know why anymore. Forgets you're there and calls for you. That frantic lunge at your name. You come running out of the shower naked and dripping wet and search his face and his body and interrogate him for answers. If you're going to help him you have to know what's wrong. He falls back in bed and catches his breath. Softens in the wake of alarm. I thought you'd left he says. You sit on the bed next to him and stroke his forehead and explain to him that you'll never leave. Ever. You promise and kiss the waxy skin of his temple. Finger his hair damp with sweat out of his eyes and smile that devastated smile. Exhausted his eyelids open and close in slow-motion until he dozes off into uneasy sleep.

This is one of the hardest parts of your day. Not the bathing. Believe it or not for this you're actually grateful. Not always. Most times you'd rather skip it frankly. It's an ordeal. You both sort of cringe when that time rolls around. Sometimes he asks if you can skip it and you tell him no. It's important. And he grudgingly caves.

But touching him. His body. His skin. Is something you've learned to cherish. There's nothing sexual about it. That quality of touch seems like an old memory whose origins you can't place. This tactile exchange between the two of you is more intimate than you thought possible. Because it is not cathartic. And for the longest time this was tough to make sense of. You want to think it's a purging experience. But that's not it at all. When you help him into the tub and wash his hands and armpits and face and hair and genitals and back and feet you each acknowledge freely that he is alive because of you. You acknowledge death without pity or fear. Which is what makes bathing him a subtly moving experience for both of you. You're telling him that you will suffer together. These quiet hours you share. Subdued and unsentimental. You're saying I love you.

What makes it difficult to deal with is seeing him like this. He's so frail. His little naked body is heartbreaking. His useless genitals are the saddest thing you've ever seen. You're ashamed of their inutility and their prominence in the constellation of anatomy that makes up the tragedy of his body. This shame unfolds and reveals ever more nuanced and abstruse layers of meaninglessness. He holds onto you for support as he steps into the tub and he trembles so badly it's hard to watch. Muscles giving under a nonexistent weight. The weight of his own body which doesn't seem to exist. He is a figment of himself. Jutting bones and hanging skin. That constant tremor that makes you want to cry. A body surrendering to itself. He finally makes it in safely and sits down and smiles. We did it he says and you love him. These insignificant afterthoughts become triumphs when you've got no strength. When walking or even standing become dangerous. Even life-threatening. Too difficult to even want to bother. You both get frustrated and bitchy. Everything is such a pain in the ass. Every little thing is an ordeal. Sometimes you want to give up. You don't tell him this. To him you say hurry up. Come on. Give me your arm. Roll over. Lift up your legs. Sit up. Sit down. Lie down. Open. Swallow. Go to sleep. I'm not going anywhere. What do you want. Stop calling me if you don't need anything. What is it. I told you. I'm right here. I'm not leaving you. Get some sleep. Close your eyes. I'm right here.

The whole ugly process is gradual so you don't notice it. But then one day you do. And nothing is the same after that. It'll be something ordinary. He'll need help to the bathroom. Won't be hungry. You'll ask a simple question. You'll say his name and he'll respond and everything will seem fine. But it's not. You just look at him. He goes what and you ask him how he feels. Fine he says. But he's not fine. Your worst fears stare back out of these eyes that belong to someone else. This is not the person you love. This is someone else entirely. That person you love is gone and isn't coming back. He looks at you and smiles and the negation of your life trails off somewhere behind that eerie gaze. You're going to throw up. This revelation metastasizes and grows into the worst pain you've ever felt. Starts in your gut and radiates outward to your fingertips and up your spine and finally makes your legs go weak. It subsumes you. You start to cry and he looks utterly puzzled. What's the matter he says. You wipe your face and smile and say nothing. He smiles and turns away. You won't admit it. You'd never forgive yourself. But part of you wants this person sitting beside you to die.

Disturbing guttural cough and the surge of alarm when you spot the blood. You do your best to calm him. You can tell he's afraid. He said he wouldn't be but he is. He should be. You're terrified but you don't tell him this. To him you say okay. We're okay. You don't know why you say 'we' but you do and continue to until the end. You think afterwards. After all this is over and all you've got is time. You think probably you said it so he wouldn't feel alone. You just don't want him to be scared. There's no getting around it for you. Your nerves will be gnawed to the dendrites for the duration. But you can ease him. You can breathe into the nape of his neck and rock him and hold his hand. But first you kick at the door. You pound your fists against the dense unforgiving obstruction and scream until your voice cracks. This scares him but you do it anyway. We need help you shout. We need help.

We need help. Pace and sob and struggle in vain to formulate a thought. Your brain will not cooperate. It's too busy turning your insides to jelly. He says come sit down so you do. You apologize. You tell him how sorry you are. He coughs again and you hold the rag for him. He says he needs to lie down. Place a pillow under his head and hold his hand. He's on his side and you stroke his arm and ask him if he needs anything. He doesn't respond. He's cold and the color has gone from his face. He jerks as if from sleep and calls your name and looks for you. I'm right here you say. You speak softly and do your best to disguise the fear in your voice. His breathing gradually becomes labored and the interval between breaths lengthens. Place a hand on his forehead and talk to him. Tell him you love him and that you're here. You're not leaving. You're right here. Last chance for whispers of love and solitude. Space between breaths a cosmos. Long and deep and frightening. And then nothing. Stillness. You kiss his hand and say come back to us. All mended. All forgiven. All ended and longed for again. ∞

Grief Settles in the Body

Laura Goldin

Like a bearing wall,
     shoring things up.

I am telling the story
my own way.

A doorframe
filling up with night;

you learn it first
and understand it later.

Geese at the lake's edge;
smell of the angled weeds, of sky.

And you might come
to love this place,

en route to somewhere
altogether new—

Holding the tapered
light aloft;

waiting a long,
     long time for it.

℣

PET CT Scan

Jennifer Chapis

According to the last horizon, obstacles.
Willow growing out of the river

drops silk onto our pillows.
Murmurs cross the deep part rushing over.

Fear: hospital at season's end.
Wind: finally lost its hair.

I feel like a tall iris in an empty field,

if not, winter.

Memorizing poems about the black masked butterfly girl
who grew up weeping,

I read *honesty* instead of *honey*.
He undid the tiny buttons on my blouse

in the way molasses inspires us
to stop feeling afraid. One cannot imagine

the river got hold of such a sagacious body.

The waiter grinding fresh pepper is not allowed to stop.

∞

"if not, winter" is borrowed from Sappho

Condensed Milk

Danielle Eigner

The unpaved mud and dust road out of town had no proper bus stop and the *tap-tap* had no schedule, but if Maralah waited long enough and was lucky, one would pass that she could hail and ride to visit her sister.

The road was cluttered with vendors who used tarps with the letters "USAID" on them to display and resell surplus goods donated from foreign countries: cheap plastic combs that she knew would bend and break in coarse, curly black hair, piles of T-shirts with slogans in English that she could not read, and bottles of cooking oil with expiration dates that had long passed. Dozens of rubber flip-flops stamped "made in Taiwan" hung from recycled yarn strung across pieces of cinderblock. From a broken-down boom box with a bent metal hanger antenna, the high-pitched pressured speech of the British sportscaster announcing the semi-final World Cup soccer match of Mexico vs. France reverberated across Port-au-Prince.

Maralah slowly flexed her arthritic knees to step over the random stuff for sale as her eyes scanned the plastic baggies of drinking water and sticks of sugar cane piled high in a crate balanced on an upside-down salvaged plastic bucket. Fried plantains made grease stains in the tabloid section of a newspaper. The essentials were sold on every street corner: phone cards, lottery tickets, and cans of condensed milk piled in the shape of an Egyptian pyramid.

When she finally spotted the condensed milk, she approached the vendor, picked up two cans from the top of the pyramid, and handed him a coin. The vendor, while balancing a transistor radio between his shoulder and ear, gave her a look of empathy and then restocked the pyramid. The static could not subdue the sportscaster's surprise as Mexico swung a free kick from the left and escaped France's defense to score within the first few minutes of the soccer match.

Maralah stood tall, looked straight ahead and held the cans of condensed milk in front of her heart as if they were candles in a Christmas procession. She had a worn look in her eyes; not only weary but also wise. Her gray-streaked hair was pulled back in a bun and wrapped in a scarf. Her skin was not brown but deep dark black with wrinkles only in the areas of expression above her eyebrows and where her lips met her cheeks.

She waited for a *tap-tap* next to a boy too old to be a child and too young to be a man. His right pant leg was cut mid-thigh, folded up and pinned to the back pocket of his jeans where his wallet would have been if he had had one. The blue veins in his forearms bulged as he transferred his weight onto his unpadded crutch to swing his only leg away from the puddle that splashed with each passing vehicle.

A *tap-tap* came into view, a converted flatbed Kia truck, honking and swerving around a scooter upon whose single seat a father, child, and mother were squeezed. "Jesus Loves You" was painted onto the upper third of the *tap-tap*'s front windshield in bright orange bubble letters, partially obstructing the driver's view. Yellow and red tassels draped down from the roof above the parallel benches of sardine-packed travelers facing each other. She would have attempted to fit her big-boned frame into any remaining crevice of space had the truck slowed down enough to board; but it did not.

The next *tap-tap* to pass was loaded with fewer people but with live poultry. She decided to let this one pass, as she was superstitious of feathered animals. The man-boy must not have been superstitious; he pulled himself into the *tap-tap* as if he were doing a pull-up in gym class. She boarded the third *tap-tap* that came, and wedged herself between a wrinkled old man and a breastfeeding mother whose infant did not appear to have the strength to suckle from the nipple between her tiny lips. From the driver's radio, the trumpet-like blast from the *vuvuzela* blared triumphantly over the cacophony of street traffic.

She bounced up and down with each pothole until Mexico scored another goal against France, at which point the driver raised both hands off the steering wheel in a gesture of either joy or rage and the road flooded with cheering people. Traffic resumed when the sea of people parted enough so that vehicles could pass, if vehicles were more aggressive than the impeding obstacles. The *tap-tap* drove past the burning trash, past the piles of cement rubble with severed wires poking out, past the football fields of tents and tarps, past the stream of sewage from which a litter of pigs grazed, to the outskirts of Port-au-Prince.

Maralah banged on the roof to signal the driver to stop, climbed over the sleeping mother and infant and out of the flatbed. She handed the driver a coin and began the mile walk to her sister's hut. She walked with the same posture she had in the city: back straight as a rod, chin up, head high, two hands holding the cans of condensed milk in front of her heart.

Her sister must have sensed that she was outside with the intuition that sisters have for each other because she opened the door and greeted her before she even knocked. In her sister's face Maralah saw her own reflection—a common past and shared losses. Maralah entered the hut through the blue tarp door and sat down on the floor where her niece Clementine lay curled in a fetal position. She tucked her knees under her round bottom and lifted Clementine's head onto her soft lap. As she combed her niece's matted hair, she softly sang the same melody her mother had sung to her many years ago when Maralah had thought that she had suffered more than she could bear.

Maralah had been probably about the same age as Clementine, nineteen, when she drank bleach, as people have done for years in Haiti. It's hard to say how old she was exactly, as she did not know the year she was born, only that there was a great hurricane. The man she considered her husband had left. Her expectation that he would have stayed was naïve; he was not legally her husband, since they had no money to pay the officials for a certificate. Nonetheless, at the time she felt that she would surely die from sorrow. But that was only a small loss. She had not truly encountered sorrow until the loss of her son. She had not known then, as she did now, that even after such dreadful sorrow the heart continues to beat, the lungs continue to breathe, and that she would carry on, bear more children, bury yet another son, and still continue to live. As an old woman, she had made her peace with sorrow as one does with a schoolyard friend who betrays and is forgiven. They were no longer in conflict but had accepted each other's presence.

Maralah's sister poked two holes in a can of condensed milk with the sharp end of the metal stake used to secure the plastic tarp floor to the dirt floor. Then she tenderly poured the milk into her defeated daughter's mouth.

After Clementine had drunk the medicinal condensed milk and the lullaby had calmed her to sleep, Maralah's sister began to tell the story of her daughter's dismay. Clementine's baby had fallen asleep and would not wake up. At first Clementine thought he was just too tired, but after a day she began to worry and brought him to her mother. Together they tried to wake him by singing to him and rubbing palm oil over his small body. He would not take of his mother's milk, and when they pried his eyelids open, they saw that his eyes were glazed and looking in opposite directions. They took him first to the local healer who chanted an incantation and prescribed an elixir. The baby would not swallow the elixir and it only dribbled from his lips, down his cheeks, and onto the dirt floor.

Then they took him to the foreign medical clinic of American doctors who came after the earthquake. In the tent with a red cross, foreigners wearing matching green pants and T-shirts swarmed the baby. They spoke loudly and poked the baby's arms and legs with needles. A Creole nurse in the same green uniform mumbled something about the baby's veins being too dried up for a water tube. They put stickers on the baby's chest, attached wires to the stickers, and attached a machine to the wires. They attached a tube to a mask that covered the baby's face and blew air into his nose and mouth. Through an interpreter they asked endless questions: Had anyone shaken the baby, hit the baby, dropped the baby? Did the baby have a heart problem, a lung problem, or a nerve problem? Did the mom take drugs, drink alcohol, or neglect the baby? After all that asking and all the machines, the interpreter said that the doctors did not know why this baby would not wake up from sleeping. The beds were full in the hospital and since they did not know how to wake the baby, they suggested going to the French clinic where there might be a doctor who could wake the baby.

Mother and grandmother swaddled the baby in a blanket, took a *tap-tap* across town, and walked the remaining distance until they found the French clinic. When they arrived, the French clinic was deserted. A blind beggar sat outside the gate with a guide stick and a tin can for coins. He must have heard them approach and by the sound of their steps knew that they needed the clinic. He said the French had left last week. The earthquake was five months past— the French had completed their mission.

Throughout the night the baby did not wake, while mother and grandmother did not sleep. They kept a hand on his chest to monitor its rise and fall. They prayed, praised, bargained, begged, sang incantations, made offerings, burned candles, shook rattles, rang bells, rubbed oils on his skin and potions on his lips. He did not wake. The next morning they took him back to the American clinic but the gate was closed and the armed guard said the clinic was closed for the World Cup. The USA was playing Algeria. By the time they returned home, the baby seemed too tired to sleep anymore. Soon after he just stopped breathing and his mother knew that he had left this world for another.

After Maralah's sister finished telling the story, they sat together outside the hut in stillness and silence. When it was time for Maralah to leave and return to the city, her sister turned to her and said, "I think my daughter drank the bleach to travel with her baby. She wouldn't have wanted him to travel to the next world alone.

But she will be okay now." Her sister handed her the remaining can of condensed milk and said, "Take it back with you, we don't need another can. It's bad luck to keep a remedy in the home. It may want to make itself useful again."

Maralah kissed her sleeping niece goodbye, embraced her sister, and then walked with her remaining can of condensed milk to the road to wait for a *tap-tap*. She stood next to a farmer hauling a metal bucket full of sugar cane to sell in the city. His arms wrapped around his cherished harvest in a protective embrace.

As the *tap-tap* inched toward the city, Maralah saw the shanties become closer and closer together, so close that one tarp was used as the wall for two adjoined neighbors. The traffic was always heavy, but never this heavy. Ghana was tied against the USA in overtime of the World Cup quarterfinal match. Crowds engulfed radios that were no longer visible but heard as muffled static among exuberant fans. And then suddenly: GOAL! The mob burst into chaos. Fireworks were launched, guns fired, cars abandoned, bottles broken, and screaming children hoisted onto shoulders. Men ran around in circles, ripping their shirts off and waving them like flags, and the chanting grew louder until the trembling earth vibrated to AF-RI-CA, AF-RI-CA, AF-RI-CA…

Maralah's fellow passengers had clawed over each other and out the window to become one with the crowd. The farmer who had moments earlier guarded his treasured sugar cane now dumped it onto the muddy road to use the metal bucket against his callused palm as a drum to the beat of AF-RI-CA, AF-RI-CA, AF-RI-CA.

Maralah found herself alone on the evacuated *tap-tap* with the lingering scent of perspiration and a discarded pile of rags that had been pushed under the bench towards the back of the *tap-tap*. Lifted by the energy of the city—once divided, now unified in jubilation—she took a deep breath, smiled, and looked out to bear witness to joy.

A faint squeak came from the bundle of rags under the bench. She did not move but waited and observed until the squeak became a cry and the cry began to move the rags. Maralah knew what she must do as only a mother would know. She reached down to the bundle of rags, unwrapped the newborn baby to see the light in his eyes. As she held him close to her chest, she prayed for the mother whose circumstance led her to abandon a child.

Comforted by Maralah's warm bosom and hypnotic heartbeat, the newborn's eyes fluttered backward and it sank into a heavy sleep. Maralah opened the can of condensed milk. She remembered how her own son would fall asleep while breast-feeding and how she would rub the roof of his mouth to encourage him to suckle. With the padded part of her little finger, she gently tapped the roof of the abandoned baby's mouth. She poured the condensed milk into her cupped palm and it dribbled down her finger into the tiny mouth, and the sleeping baby began to feed. &

Uses for Salt

Kate Lynn Hibbard

To remove mildew from linen, moisten the spot with salt and
soap, place out in the sun until stain is removed.

When I was married, the older women, they used Vaseline a lot.

To remove tea stains on cups, rub salt on spots.

They said a greased egg wouldn't hatch.

To prevent blueing from streaking clothes, put a handful of salt
in last rinsing water.

And then of course we were more or less a little bit careful.

It will also keep them from sticking to the line on a frosty day.

I suppose the Catholics called it the rhythm.

To make a candle burn longer, fill with salt around the wick, up to
the blackened part.

We were told as long as you nursed a baby you wouldn't conceive.

Remedy for colic—dissolve 1 teaspoonful each salt and black
pepper (ground) in a glass of cold water. Drink as much as
possible and lie down. Repeat the dose if necessary.

And then a lot of them used salt.

To remove ink stains, salt is good for carpets or woolen goods.

The kind they put in ice cream. Rock salt.

Cover the stain and let stand a few minutes then brush off lightly and add clean salt and brush vigorously.

I never did use the rock salt.

In most cases the stain will disappear.

We were told it affected the mind.

To prevent hair from falling out—put 2 tablespoonfuls of salt on paper and with a stiff brush dipped in it rub the scalp.

There was a lady that come through one time, and she had a receipt.

A dash of salt improves the taste of coffee.

She took cocoa butter and boric acid.

Clean brass, copper and pewter with paste made of salt and vinegar, thickened with flour.

And you made these little cones and you'd use those.

Soak stained handkerchiefs in salt water before washing.

We made them together.

Sprinkle salt on your shelves to keep ants away.

Oh yes, it worked.

∞

April 1986, Ukraine

Laurel Bastian

First explosion blows the roof.
Second starts a graphite fire.

Extinguishing it is fairly simple
chemistry: drop boron and lead from the sky.

Harder is extinguishing coals lodged
inside people who cannot help

their porousness, who can't redirect
the laden clouds inching

overhead in Nowosibkov,
stuttering drops of poison down.

Cataclysm can't be taken lightly,
however weightless we become.

Death sleeps in the corners
of every live body. It detonates,

precisely. If it didn't mean our human
end, we might take the glowing,

swollen throat, the blown
system, charged space where before

there was form,
the clock's hand easing

past the last notch
as miraculous.

The Day of the Surgical Colloquium Hosted by the Far East Rand Hospital

Gill Schierhout

Three months ago I lost my hand in a mining accident. Doctor sewed it on again. Now here I am at this Medical Conference, a marvel, picking up cotton reels, tying bits of string. Doctor is saying something, pointing to pictures of my x-rays that are projected up on a big white screen, like the drive-in.

Strange seeing the stump of your wrist bloated up to twenty times its usual size, projected up there on the wall. I don't recall giving anyone permission to take that picture. There's no doubt it's my limb though. See, the same tattoo as on my forearm; the ink has sunk deep, its pinpricks of blue show up like the pores of a giant orange up there on the wall. I consider whether or not to roll up my sleeves so that at least in the tea break the audience can see it's me—but then I'd have to take my jacket off and Doreen made me promise to keep it on. I just sit, waiting, like in church. Big holes of sweat are forming under my armpits.

Doctors are here from all over: Jo'burg General, Helen Joseph, Bloem, Chris Hani Baragwanath, everywhere man. You can tell from the labels they've pinned to their coats.

Must be a good lens on that doctor's camera to take pictures like these. I wouldn't mind a better camera myself. One day I'd like to set up a darkroom in the house, do the developing, play tricks with the light, put heads on bodies that do not match. I've seen this in the photographic magazines in the hospital waiting room. I imagine Doreen as a twin. I could do with two wives—I'd let them grimace at one another, identical in blackened tooth, across the picture.

Every week Doreen does the crossword from the Sunday papers, and then she posts it off. They put all the entries into a hat and the first correct one to be drawn wins a lot of cash. She's never won the crosswords, to my knowledge, but she says it keeps her mind active. Recently she's taken to doing Sudoku too, but there's no cash prize there, it's just the challenge.

"If someone else can do it, Frank, so can I," she says.

A severed hand is quite popular, it seems, but all the fuss over me is going to stop if I lose my head. No one wants to know you then. Like Geezer—he was an average sort of bloke, until the day he and his team were trapped underground for 26 days. He was the sole survivor. The pillars were mined too thin and the roof collapsed. Now he walks around with sticks in his hair, talking to himself. It depends on where you mine and how deep you go as to the size the pillars have to be. Under this hospital, for example, it's all mined. There's more stress here: the vibrations, the tonnage of the trucks on the main road, the expansion and contraction. And the safety factor is higher—you can't take out too much of the pillars.

Perhaps one day Geezer'll come right, wake up and comb his hair. Doreen thinks so. She leaves him pots of food sometimes, out on the front step. He comes carefully, like an animal not yet tamed. I tell her not to waste. She just scowls, her face screwed tighter than the cloth she uses to wipe the washed floor dry. A colony lives off that man. The day he dies he'll decompose faster than a rotten cabbage. Every mine has its idiot.

From where I am sitting, I can see the sign stuck on the door of this room, hand-written, big easy letters:

Conference Room. Surgical Colloquium.

A big red arrow points inside.

The doc is showing a picture of my hand—how it was before he sewed it on again. The hand is carefully laid out in its plastic bag on a wide strip of tissue paper; it looks as big as a corpse up there on the wall. It reminds me of a picture of Doreen that I have somewhere at home: she is in the garden, standing in front of last year's mielies. I had put her there to show the height of the crop that we planted beside the house. Man, they towered above her, and she's a tall woman, big-boned too, tallest maize plants you'll ever see. I remember picking up that picture not too long ago and noticing for the first time how her face was all creased up against the sun. She looked middle-aged, and quite worn out, standing there in a yellow Sunday dress and matching hat. A wife can seem so much part of a man.

Thinking of that picture now, I have a curious feeling, like something is missing—a phantom pain. There is a sharp tick-ticking sound. I look up. It is just the Colloquium sign flapping in a sudden gusty breeze.

Doctor has taken out a small torch now. He's using it to point to the pictures on the wall. The pin-prick torch beam hovers above the thin pale tendons—they hang from the severed wrist like roots off a turnip. One of the doctors is blowing his nose on a large handkerchief, a frown across his brow. He turns his head briefly to face the window. Then he looks again at the slide show up on the wall. I remember what someone once told me, that a man tried to lip-print a thousand cows—each lip print was examined and found to be different from every other one. It is the same with humans; we are all made different, it is only our culture and education that makes us appear the same.

A new picture is flashed up now, a cross-ways view through my bones. Doctor drones on. That's such a clean cut through my hand. That 80kg rock splintered from the face had an edge sharper than the blade of a knife. Doreen and I, we've got one child—a boy— there's another kid on the way, and each day she doesn't know if I'm going to come home again after the shift. I don't know how she does it. I don't know how she doesn't crack.

Doreen is not the sort to raise her voice. Last week she threw a bowl of pap and gravy right at my head. I don't recall what I did to trigger it—I must have done something wrong. It didn't turn into a fight that time, though. I just went outside, gave her time to cool off.

I went underground the day I turned sixteen. Mining wasn't my first choice. I wanted to be a fitter and turner, but there were no positions. You can earn twice as much underground as on the surface, that's why I've stuck it out this long. Sometimes I stand at the main station and look up at the square of daylight, and, at night, sometimes see the stars. The square of light is 300 metres up; stars much higher. There is a longing I have, a longing built in for sunlight. Perhaps it is every miner's dream to own a farm.

When I met Doreen I was nineteen, just got my blasting certificate. She had passed her Matric and soon after she got a good job in bookbinding. I was working at Dannhauser, Natal. There we worked 11¾ hours a day, some regulation not allowing us to work 12 hours every day. Saturday was half-day, we worked only 9 hours, got drunk Saturday night, slept late on Sunday and back to work on Monday. Payday or nearest Friday we hired a car and went to Dundee where the shops stayed open until nine at night. Used to go to Dannhauser station to check on passengers or just to see the trains come in and out. After working underground for a few years I'd saved enough to buy a motorcycle. Doreen liked riding pillion, the faster the better. Until the day I lost my hand.

First thing I saw was the blood in fountains. I yelled out. Twin fountains gushing from inexhaustible veins, coursing from rivers that will never run dry. I tried to stop the fountain, pressing as close to the source as I could. My hand came right off; it was hanging by a bit of skin. And then it fell. I picked it up and called my mates; one led in front to stop me falling down the stope, one came behind to push a bit. I was holding the left hand with the right, using the hand to squash the blood, stop it shooting up to the roof, but whatever I did, it flooded. I passed the first-aid station, swore, wouldn't let anyone touch me, passed the second medical depot at the top, swore no one to touch me until I got to the hospital. Passed out, then came around the next day. I've been here before, 133 broken bones and counting. I am no stranger at the Far East Rand Hospital.

"Just keep breathing," Doreen once told me.

At that time I was lying in hospital with a broken collarbone and four crushed ribs.

"Just keep breathing Frank. One day things will come right."

And that's the longest speech I've ever heard her say. Doreen's not the sort to waste her words (only our food, on Geezer). But something else happened underground that day—it took weeks before I realised it. They are always going on about safety at the mine. A miner tests each working place every day, and uses chalk to write the date on the hanging wall. Only then is the team allowed in that area to work.

I've always been a leftie. I didn't expect Doctor to sew my left hand on, but after he did, I taught the hand to do everything it used to: buttons and zips and folding papers, and building up the strength by squeezing rubber balls. By now I can do almost anything, even tie knots in pieces of string.

But something changed for me: I can't write. Not left or right or toes or mouth. The muscles are here, the brain pumps out its thoughts, but whatever it is that takes the words from the brain to the hand to form the letters has gone.

I first saw Doctor Morar from the back. He was facing away from me, attending to the bloke in the bed opposite. Doctor is a big man, tall, bald as an egg, so that when he turned around and came towards me, I was surprised how young he looked—young, but tired.

"I want the dough, Doc," I said, pointing with my good hand to the other one laid out on the plastic and crushed ice beside me. "I won't beg for it, but I am telling you I want a way to get out. I'll try something new—anything on the surface."

I had in mind to live a healthy sort of a life in the light with plenty of fresh air. Surely the loss of a hand is worth a living wage for a miner?

But after the surgery, when it finally came to do the paperwork required by the Compensation Board, Doc did not agree. He was so pleased with his work in sewing my hand back on again, that he refused to sign. Back to work with me.

My name is down for tomorrow's early shift, clocking in at 4:00 a.m. to water the stopes before the team comes in at 6. Then

I'll be ahead of the boys, hitting the hanging for loose pieces of rock, sounding it for blisters or bad hanging—loose pieces must be barred down and every place made safe. Yet that day it happened there was no warning—we'd worked in that stope for two weeks already. It just cracked.

The storm is breaking now, the beautiful Jo'burg downpour of fresh angled rain sounding on the roof outside. The rain bounces on the tarmac, and the sky has broken open and the rain falls in torrents on the roof of the hall and already the gutters are overflowing, the rain spilling over their sides like sand.

I watch the back of Doctor's head from this strange angle. He'd talked me into it, how fine it would be to be on stage. The skull is made up of 29 different bones, the occupational therapist had once told me. Meanwhile, the hand only has 24. He's got a cheek this doctor, showing me off like some prize bull. Sure, my hand works again, good as new. I can wield a hammer, flip a switch, pronate and supinate the wrist with the best of them, tie knots in pieces of string.

Yes, it's true he sewed my hand back on again. My fingers close around the ball of string waiting here in my jacket pocket. With the rain come sheets of lightning, and more and more rain and lightning, and it's suddenly fresh and cool. Doctor carries on with his lecture, as if nothing at all has happened.

It was the hardest thing I've ever done to get out of that stope. There was no oxygen, and the top of the hand hanging by a bit of string, and the blood. You breathe, and there's nothing there, like breathing cotton wool, breathing nothing. Perhaps it was the shock, the loss of blood, but something in my brain has gone.

I don't think I ever passed Standard Six. I'm not like Doreen, she's very clever. But it still feels peculiar to be unable to write. No doing. Do any of these doctors have any idea what it's like? To have rising up inside you the things you need to get down: the shopping, the list of stuff you need to remember to do, the parts to buy, the date on the hanging wall, but no way to put it down? A bit of my brain must have died there in the shaft with no oxygen.

Some of them down in the audience are nodding and smiling now. I wasn't paying attention. Doctor must have been talking about me. I must get ready to do my demonstration. The sweat at the armpits is cooling through my suit. I didn't expect to sweat today, not out here on the surface where things are easy, not here in this fancy place. Miners sweat a lot on account of the atmosphere; we pour the sweat from our boots after the shift. I have a little competition going between the left and right boot, to see which is holding more. It's a part of your brain that actually forms the letters, isn't it? I must focus on the string, not worry about the letters.

Doctor is tugging at my suit jacket. He takes my elbow as if to steer me like an old woman, towards the podium. I am supposed to walk now to the table and do my show. I pull myself together.

"I'm no invalid," I say.

Still he walks with me to the table then pats me on the shoulder. Some of them nod and smile again. The water on the iron roof is making such a racket I can't hear my own thoughts in here. I'm supposed to show them how I can tie knots in pieces of string: a figure-of-eight; reef knot; granny knot; slippery hitch—any knot you like. And then I'm supposed to pick up cotton reels and do some knitting. The occupational therapist made me do it every afternoon in the hospital, "…to strengthen the 24 muscles you have in your hand. Doctor's orders," she said. I thought she was quite keen on me the way she carried on.

And now I'm supposed to show them the splints they made me; each finger with its own sling and spring.

"How do you feel about your hand, Frank?" Doctor beams from his teeth.

When my voice comes through the microphone, it's full of breath like fuzz.

"Talk to the audience," he instructs. "Do you think you can work again?"

He takes his hand from my shoulder and leaves me there in the centre of the stage. He is sitting down now, arms folded across his stomach. This is piss easy, man. I see it clear as anything. It's peaceful now, with the rain on the roof, and all these clever men smiling and listening to me. The world is almost sweet.

When I speak, it is only to try to make the tremble in my voice shut up. It is only to try to make the breath steady up, that I begin to talk. I hold the microphone just as I saw the doctor hold it, just right, and I blow into it, and I smile.

"To answer Doctor's question, yes, I can work again, Doc."

I look across the audience, sitting there, some with pens poised to take notes.

"Some other time," I say, just to keep talking, just to keep my voice from losing itself to the shudder of the ground beneath us. "Some other time I will tell you what happened the day I lost my hand, what it was like. It's nothing really, accidents happen all the time below the surface. I know you've come here to see me tie bits of string."

Fair is fair: I got my hand back, I can't have the cash. But I want to tell them that I can no longer write. I want to tell them how I have tried, sitting up with Doreen and the crossword and a pen, crying in rage, day after day, I want to tell them what it's like. But I am afraid that if I start to blubber, the weeping will never stop. Doreen lies like a corpse in bed beside me night after night. Is it because of this business with my hand, that she thinks I am some kind of idiot now?

I take a breath. I put my hand in my pocket to pull out the string for the show. There is a pen here too. Just a piece of paraphernalia that the mine gives out for free, along with a handful of condoms in your pay packet. It has a slogan printed on the side:

"AIDS is Real. Time to Change."

I carefully place the pen and the string on the podium beside the mike. I take the ball of string and cut the first length. The doctor's camera zooms in on my hand. Up behind me, a live video of the hand has commenced, projected up there on the wall so that everyone can see exactly how my muscles move. I tie the first knot and the audience applauds. I nod. Nice and slow, I cut myself a second length of string. I am doing just fine.

Then the storm breaks—lightning sheets across the faces in front of me—and the picture of my hand behind me dissolves altogether into a gray-black wall. The remaining breath is squeezed out of the projector and its lights in a final hum. The audience begin to murmur and scrape their chairs. In a few minutes the storm will be over—what will be left is the sound of the rain on the roof, and the drip drip drip of those inadequate gutters onto the paving.

No point in carrying on with this if they can't see what I'm doing. If I ever have a chance to build myself a house I'll give generous gutters, proper generous gutters that hold the water and that flow into a rainwater tank. And I'll build the house so it faces north with a good sunroom, too, for Doreen to warm up on those late winter afternoons when we get old. She's always had poor circulation, such cold hands and feet.

I look up and see that the doctor is waving the hand-function spring-thing in front of my face—the contraption they made, just for me, to get my hand to work again. Okay, I have forgotten to do that part of the demonstration.

"Sorry about the power," he says to the audience. Without the help of the microphone, the Doctor's voice is a little lone cry at the edge of the world.

"Before we wrap up, I would like to demonstrate how the resistance experienced both in flexion and extension at the metacarpal joints…"

I watch him as if through a gauze, a safety net. I shake my head. Instead of taking the hand-function contraption he is trying to put on me, I pull my hand away. I pick up the AIDS pen and hold it out to him.

"You keep this, Doc, you may as well have it," I say. "You've done a good job here, on my hand, Doc. Congratulations."

The doctor reaches out as if to take the pen, but really just to shut me up, and send me on my way so that everyone can applaud him.

"Give the brave man a hand."

I have something to say. I am still holding the pen, only just stopping myself from throwing it at him. My voice comes out much louder than I expect it to, a flood of anger shooting the words out of my body.

"This hand he's put on me—it does not remember how to write. I cannot even sign my name."

I push over the stupid little podium. The hard edge of it falls against the metal leg of an empty chair in the front row. The docs to either side draw back, their torsos pulling away from the noise. In the clatter, I give the table a kick for good measure.

I look across at the audience. From the expressions on their faces, they've not seen a bit of life in this place for quite some time. I brace myself to step down and lay a fist across a face or two. I look at the short, fat one from Helen Joseph, and the one next to him with his stethoscope tucked in his pocket.

No, I must back down. I must stay calm. I return, shaking, to my small seat at the side of the stage. Every mine has its idiot.

I count three slow drips from the gutters and then the twittering from the audience begins. I can't hear too well what they are saying as some have started pushing and scraping their chairs.

"Come to my clinic on Tuesday, I'll sort you out."

I look across the room but I cannot see who has spoken.

"He's a miner," I think I hear someone mutter. "Why does a miner need to write?"

"Use the other hand," the doctor in the row behind me says. He smiles. "You have another hand."

Something else is said from the back. A gust of laughter sweeps through the room.

Outside, Doctor finds me. He gives me a bit of cash, as a 'thank you' and offers me a lift. He says it has to be quick because he needs to get back to the conference dinner.

"I'd like some fresh air," I say. "I've never seen such a lot of jerks in one place in all my life."

I step carefully across the world all heavy with damp, the rain all stopped now. The leaves on the trees are so laden that a breeze or bump sends another shower beneath. I take off my jacket as I walk and sling it over the back of my shoulder. The doc's thank-you is burning a hole in my pocket. The Queen's Hotel is on my way home. A broken bottle is lying near the gutter at the hotel entrance. I could kill someone with that bottle.

I think of those doctors' faces in front of me, and Doctor Morar droning on. He reminds me of a bulldog I used to have. Her name was Sally. I had to shoot her because she wouldn't let go of a black kid in the street. I felt bad about that, really bad—about shooting the dog, and about the kid. Police made me do it. I turn into the bar to wash the taste of the mine from my mouth.

Sometimes because of the brandy, Doreen and I have our differences of opinion, but I've never hit her. Well, since losing my hand, to be honest I've come pretty close. I'm sorry about it though, she knows I'm sorry. I know I haven't really been myself since this business.

Our house comes into view. A figure is swinging back and forth on the gate. It's our boy, nine years old, way past his bedtime. His bare feet are hooked in through the chicken wire. He calls from down the street.

"Where's my mother?"

As I come closer I see his eyes are swollen. He is trying to hide his tears through anger and grumbling. And his clothes are drenched through as if he's stood here through several storms. Water drips from his chin, his nose.

"What took you so long? I'm hungry, Dad, I'm starved. Mom's gone."

"Where is your mother?"

Ray follows me indoors like a dog. The golden liquid I've just imbibed slides me through the house. They say that skin is waterproof, but the scalp, so thickly imbued with oil, must be the most watertight of all, to stop the falling rain.

There is her absence—a bottle of shampoo missing from the bathroom shelf, her yellow Sunday dress gone from its hanger, a space on the shelf where a picture used to stand—Ray, last Christmas, holding the pellet gun we gave him. The crossword puzzle sits unfinished in Doreen's top drawer. Beside it, her small folded umbrella. There is no note.

A little later I hear a scraping at the door, like an animal wanting to come in. I tell Geezer to bugger off. He scatters like seed into the dark wet night.

After Ray is in bed, hugging his pellet gun, I check again. I turn the house upside down but there is no note. A wife is supposed to leave a note, that's how they do it in the movies. ∾

My Father's False Memory of His Mother

Brian David Mooney

She made better meatloaf than anyone,
cooking in her kitchen-Irish kitchen.
She wasn't of the lace-curtain Irish.
She was potato-Irish through and through.
"John, be worth more than it'll cost your sons
to bury you," she said. I did my best.
I was born so premature that to keep
me alive she kept me in the cookpan.
She stowed that pan in her big white oven,
sang lullabies to that big stove belly.
I did my best in the stove's slow blue heat,
stoking the furnace of my too-small heart.
How she cooed as I moved in that cookpan,
more man than meatloaf, more meatloaf than man.

&

Minivan

Anne Valente

Jane hovers in front of the mirror sometimes, when she thinks I'm not looking. Tweezers in her left hand, a mat of hair raised in her right, she homes in on a single gray strand nobody can see, laid low against her scalp, a needle in the haystack of her heavy, dark waves. She plucks the colorless ones, releases them down to the trash can below our bathroom curtains, sometimes with brown strays she's been careless to remove. When she's satisfied with this, she replaces the tweezers in our medicine cabinet, next to my razors and aftershave.

Two of her gray hairs stick to the curtains, silvery white against the muted green fabric as I brush my teeth, something I used to do while walking around the apartment, making the bed or putting dishes away, but Jane tells me now that this makes her nervous. It's annoying, she says, like pacing. So I hunch over our cramped bathroom sink, my mouth all foam in the tiny vanity mirror, and maintain perfect eye level with the hairs, two stragglers that floated the wrong way on their slow journey down.

In the bedroom Jane huddles against the headboard, knees pulled to her chest, a pair of noise-canceling headphones hugging her ears. They are mine, a pair I bought just after college three years ago when we lived in a box-like studio together. I used to plug them into the television when Jane wanted to read in silence. The headphone cord snakes from the sheets, across the carpet to our stereo, and this behavior of hers is also new, something I'd have noticed earlier if she let me pace around, brushing.

I curl up beside her, tap her shoulder like a door. She turns, her cheek soft against my hand, and pulls a speaker back from her ear.

"These are nice, Jon," she says. "They drown out the world."

And before I can answer, she pulls them off and turns out the light. "It's like I'm not even here," she says through the dark.

A month ago, when the early May sun at last banished all threat of snow from Chicago, Jane started a garden. I found her standing with her cereal, watching our feeble patch of patio grass, and two days later she'd dug up a small square in the farthest corner of our already-small lot, her palms and knees black with loam, hiding scars that were just beginning to heal. Not a real garden—just two small cherry tomato plants, marked by stakes she hoped they'd climb. She nurtured them inside first, seating them in the living room as we watched old movies, then transplanted them outside, showering them with water. She gravitates that way now, nearly every day after we eat dinner. I let her go alone.

I've asked her if she wants help, but she always shakes her head no. And I don't push this—I can't—in case she thinks I view her as a victim like everyone else does, as someone who can't save herself.

When I come home late from school, after an exhibit for the parents to see what their kids have been working on, Jane is sitting in the living room, feet propped on our ottoman, shins stained pink with calamine lotion.

"Poison ivy," she says, reaching forward to scratch. "The tomatoes were a bad idea."

I glance out the window, see her cherry tomatoes are just starting to appear, small globes like pale green gumballs, weeks from blooming to ripe.

"I don't know about that." I sit beside her, inspect the bright red bumps poking up from beneath the lotion. "This will go away. You'll have tomatoes all summer."

She leans forward, like she doesn't hear me. "I wish I could graft skin," she says. "I wish I could scrape this rash right off me." She looks at the bumps. "Motherfuckers."

Her fingers clench, her nails extend. I nudge her hands aside before she can scratch the flaked pink away.

Jane asks about work, what parents said about this round of paintings. She even asks about Toby, her favorite student of mine, the smallest boy in the second grade with the biggest pair of glasses. She thought he was precious, so small he could fit in her pocket, the times she stopped by on her days off from the hair salon to see what I did all day. She hasn't come by at all for summer session, hasn't wanted to be around the kids, their collages, their colorful fingerprints smudged into the rough texture of paper. She hasn't asked about Toby in almost two months.

I haven't brought this up, or anything else, and won't until she is ready. But I've seen her look away when we pass strollers on the street, or when children stand before us in the grocery line, pulling Mars bars from the convenience shelf before their mothers can see them. I've seen her watch them, her tongue moving inside her mouth across the chip in her left canine, one she hides now with close-lipped smiles so no one will ask.

We haven't gone to the movie theater either for the past two months. We went only once, back in April, to take her mind off the wave of lineups the police put her through, after she decided to prosecute against their advice. But when the lights dimmed and the previews began, I heard her breath accelerate inside the dark. When I reached across the seat, I found her fingers gripping the armrest. She whispered she might faint, and we left before she could. The darkness is what it was. So much dark like so many sidewalks, unlit by so few streetlamps.

I ask Jane how her day was, but she brushes off the question and watches her blooming rash instead, says client flow has been slow lately. Summer vacationers, people letting their hair grow wild in the warmer months, though I wonder if her boss has lightened her load, a gradual ease back to work after taking all of last month off. Jane is the reason I haven't paid for a haircut in over five years, but even this has gone by the wayside lately. My head feels overgrown, shaggy in the back by the ears, but to even ask her now for this favor, it feels horribly frivolous. It can wait until August, when the new class of kids will come in, and by then enough time will have passed. By then, summer's unbearable fluidity will have browned into the crisp edge of fall, and a new season will maybe feel like a new life.

After dinner, Jane spends most of the evening outside—not gardening, the patch is still too small—but reading, though each time I look out the window she's watching the sky instead, a nightfall still too new for stars. She stares into the black, darkening heavily above a tinted horizon, and reaches forward every so often with fingers extended above the rash, like she wants to scratch her legs raw.

I mentioned last month that maybe she should see a therapist. I said it gently, but meant it with resolution. Therapy seemed like a requirement. But she glared at me and turned away, and said over her shoulder, mouth muffled into skin, *But I was just walking by. They should be in fucking therapy, if anyone is.*

I am reading in bed when she finally comes in from the yard. I hear the screen door open and close, and then she is nestled into the sheets beside me, her head resting on my shoulder, the headphones discarded on the floor at least for tonight.

"Breastbone," she says, her palm laid flat on my chest.

It's something she once said after we'd just met, the first time she'd ever touched me in a way that wasn't platonic. We were lying on my bed when she reached over, she placed her hand on my sternum and said it, *breastbone,* and the shape of that word in her mouth felt like that spot had existed without description until she named it.

Her hand stays on my chest even after she falls asleep. And this, these glimmers, like stars falling through the dark until they disintegrate, this is what I cling to, to know the Jane I knew is there.

A week passes before she brings home a gun. It is there on the kitchen counter when I return from work, a Glock handgun, and I look away when I imagine her palms enclosing its rough grip. She mentioned this possibility just once, when we were walking home from the park last month after dusk and she slowed her pace along the sidewalk, looked off toward the lighted windows of apartments above the storefronts we passed. She wanted something reliable without intricate parts, something uncomplicated that would react immediately if the need arose. I told her then that it made me uncomfortable, that she didn't need a gun, but the one word I should have said, the one suspended all these weeks above the permit fees, the background check, the paperwork she must have completed without telling me, is the one I can't say to her now. No. That word has fallen from my mouth, like too many ice cubes, overcrowded by the implication of what it could mean inside the snail shell chambers of her ears.

Jane walks in from the living room, and for just a moment she is an intruder and this, her gun, a disorientation that spills a prickling down my arms. She's never home from the salon before I return from school.

"I took the afternoon off," she says. Her hands find the countertop, just inches from the grip and I look away again. I don't know what to say.

"Look, I know you disagree." She sighs, as if I'm a parent who's taken away her driving privileges. "That's why I didn't tell you."

A quiet cloud rolls into my brain when she says this, some muddled rage with no source, no culprit, not her or me though we are here anyway, as if on the other side, a new world where we make decisions we never dreamed of and Jane buys a gun while I teach my class of second graders how to watercolor.

"So, what?" I try not to yell. "You're going to carry this around with you? A gun-slinging straight-shooter?"

She looks at me, and her eyes burn the way they did when I first walked into the room at the hospital, a wind-whipped, bitter morning just past the official start of spring. When they finally let me see her, after the nurses gathered the kit, the samples and scrapings and swabs she still hasn't talked about, and at last helped her shower.

I tell her I'm sorry, drop my workbag to the floor and move around the counter, place a hand between her shoulder blades. She leans into my chest, and over the top of her head I can see my hand, there on the fabric of her shirt—small-seeming, insignificant, no better protection than a wooden spoon, not then and not now.

Jane stays inside after dinner, resists the pull of the tomato garden crimsoning pea green to scarlet, and sits beside me on the couch, her hand skirting my stomach. These small affections, our shared convergences, they are enough for now because they must be. We haven't made love much at all since March, only once or twice in cautious movements, and she softened into sobs each time, her broken tooth biting her lip, slow tears as if she didn't want to hurt my feelings, to say this wasn't right.

I want to tell her I am not them. I want to tell her I am safe. But I hold my breath, those words seem useless, they are things she must already know, of course she knows. She knows more than I will ever know.

People have asked me how I feel, *oh you must be so angry,* in moments when Jane isn't around. And I nod, tell them yes, and change the subject with a different kind of anger, that they expect me to be anything at all. Because the truth is that I feel close to nothing. Not anger, no impulse for revenge, not the restless twinge of retribution, no baseball bats tucked away in my trunk. What I feel instead is helpless, completely inert and static, like her motions and movements are things I should have guarded more carefully, and that negligence will blanket me like a fine, irremovable powder forever.

I also wonder sometimes, when I look at Jane across the dinner table or while she's asleep and I'm not, if maybe I don't believe this actually happened. I knew of violence but not random, unchecked brutality, a violence that makes me sorry to inhabit this world, to know the impulse exists. She was just walking home, the three blocks from the subway to our apartment. Eight at night, the late-March sun was gone, but the sky wasn't even fully black when they screeched up in a minivan, the one grabbed her and shoved her inside the backseat, the other held the wheel. It must have taken seconds, not long enough for anyone to notice, but they drove around for two hours, taking turns, and when they finally pushed her from the van, somewhere south in some residential neighborhood, a middle-aged man found Jane unconscious on his lawn and called the police.

That is all I know. I don't push it, not past this brief nutshell the cops gave me, after I called them when she never came home, never answered her phone, after they called back that she'd finally been found, that she was at the hospital and I might want to sit down before they told me what happened.

People have asked, *Don't you want to know?* My colleague Tim, he said over lunch about his ex-girlfriend, *When Susie fucked that guy from her gym, I wanted to know everything about it. How many times, whether he fucked better than me, what kind of mattress and where, or if they just tore their clothes off in the goddamn car.* I'd thrown out my half-eaten lunch; the world he lived in was so far apart from my own. I told him to go fuck himself, something I regretted later in case my students had overheard me.

Jane says she'll keep the gun inside, that she won't carry a concealed weapon in her purse. I wonder what the point is, if she never felt unsafe at home. But as we sit there watching television, and Jane shoulders herself deeper against my side, I think I see it exactly from her eyes. I was the safety of home, a protection that failed. I was made of unreliable parts.

Jane pushes herself up from the couch, and I avoid her eyes, watch her shins instead. Her rash has died away to a visible redness without the itch, and for a moment there is comfort in this, that the passage of time can transform and remove.

"It's late. I'm brushing my teeth." She turns off the television. "I'll be in bed in a minute."

And on my way to the bedroom, though the bathroom door is half-closed, I can see her inside hovered low and squinting deep into the mirror, her tweezers suspended above her head to purge what doesn't belong, hulking unseen beneath the hairline.

At school, Toby asks where Miss Jane has been. He asks offhandedly, while dipping strips of newspaper in paste and cementing them to a balloon, but the feigned nonchalance of children lets me know he misses seeing her. For a moment I want to pick him up, to forget the rules of classroom conduct and pull his small face to mine, tell him he is wise and how much we share. But I nod at his papier-mâché instead, tell him he's on the right track, and say Jane has been sick but she'll hopefully come by soon. Toby looks up at me, and through his thick glasses I can see why Jane has stayed away. Toby knows I am lying.

This week we are making piñatas, and each student has blown up a balloon to paste with newspaper, to paint as clowns or planet Earths or cartoonish self-portraits. So far two kids have whispered concerns to me about leaving a hole big enough for candy, once we pop the balloons. Sam worries he'll forget to leave an opening entirely, and Caroline thinks that Snickers bars, her favorite candy, might be too large for her tiny gourd-shaped piñata.

While the kids color as they wait for their balloons to dry, Althea approaches my desk and asks if it will be hard to paste the hole shut, once the candy is safely inside. When I look up and see the anxiety creased between her eyebrows, I wish with every strand of my stretched-thin heart that I was her, if only for a moment. But when I see her knotted knuckles, clamped hard around her paintbrush, the feeling passes. I tell Althea we will seal the piñatas the same way we made them, once the papier-mâché has dried and there is nothing to worry about.

On the subway home I think about Jane's gun. She keeps it in her bedside drawer, claims she barely knows how to pull a trigger, but that she'd know if the need came, she'd be ready this time around. A flood of passengers enters the train, and when I move over a seat to let an older woman sit down near the aisle, I catch my reflection in the subway car's panoramic windows. July is halfway gone, and the new students will be arriving in just a few more weeks. My hair is longer than I thought, unruly and disheveled.

Since Jane won't be home for another hour anyway, I stop by the Super Cuts a few blocks from our apartment. Jane claims places like this are what made her a stylist, after one incidence in particular when a Fantastic Sam's cut bangs to her hairline. But what I need is simple, a trim straight across. Just enough for presentable parent-teacher conferences in August, and nothing someone here couldn't do.

The hairstylist seats me in front of a mirror and begins trimming away, dipping the comb in water every so often to straighten the strands and cut.

"You've got split ends." She meets my eyes in the mirror. "Been awhile since you've had it cut?"

And all I can do is nod, before she pushes my chin down to trim the back.

At home, the tomatoes have ripened into bright red gumdrops almost overnight, so I pull four from their vines, to surprise Jane and show her the garden wasn't futile. The poison ivy near the plants has receded away, so far that Jane could even plant more vegetables if she wanted, maybe mums or squash for fall.

The tomato salads I've made are ready when Jane walks through the door, sets her bag down and sits at the table. I start to tell her about the piñatas, the kids' worried questions because I know she'll laugh, and the roster for the new semester, enrollment will be up. I want to tell her too that Toby asked about her, but I hesitate before the words come.

It is only when I set the salads on the table that I notice she hasn't responded. She is staring at me instead, her mouth set, eyes tapered into slits.

"You got your hair cut," she says. She doesn't look away.

"Well, yeah. For the fall."

Jane's jaw shifts beneath her skin, teeth clenched in a movement I've come to know as anger. "Why didn't you just ask."

"You've been busy. I didn't want to bother you."

"Bullshit, Jonathan." My full name, only when she is furious.

"It's just a haircut," I tell her. "Really, it's not a big deal."

"Oh, my poor girlfriend." Her voice mocks mine. "My girl-friend's so fucking fragile that I won't even ask her for a haircut, the same goddamn haircut I've had for years and years."

The room falls quiet then, a silence with space for me to begin to understand.

"Do you know what the police asked me, before you got there?"

I don't know what to say to this. We are characters in a flip book, we've switched scenes entirely.

"Why were you walking home alone, a pretty girl like you?" Her voice is mocking again. "You city girls and your sundresses, you always think you can take care of yourselves."

She's never told me what they said, or anything else about that night. I step closer to her, and she steps away.

"You want to know what happened to my tooth?" She grins at me, but it's not a smile. I can see the chip, its jagged void. I shake my head no. There is nothing I want to know less.

"I punched the first guy in his goddamn face, when he tried to push me down. That's when he slammed my face into the car window."

These are things I cannot hear. These are things I will think about in detail, for days and months and years.

"I saw that minivan again, Jon." She is staring at me. Adrenaline tingles, explodes through my arms. "I saw it again two weeks ago. I wanted a gun before the police would ever do anything about it."

I hesitate, toddler steps, I am learning to walk. "Why didn't you tell me?"

She hears me though my voice falters, though I barely speak.

"Because you're no different," she says, and my heart is an egg, shell fragile hiding yolk, more fragile than she'll ever be as she moves past me and out the door.

I am in bed, listening to my headphones that are now hers, when I hear her come home. The volume is low though I want to hear it anyway, this retreat from the world, lights out so I understand the same darkness too. But when Jane walks into the bedroom, she flips on the light and stares at me. Her face indicates some threshold, like she wants to tell me something or I should begin first.

"That haircut sucks," she finally says. She approaches me tentatively, then grabs my wrist and leads me to the bathroom.

Once I am seated in a chair, over bathroom tiles for easy cleaning and she's sprayed my hair with water, Jane moves around my head determining how to shape it, how to fix this devastating blunder. She doesn't speak to me, doesn't even look me in the face but concentrates instead, her chipped tooth biting the edge of her lip.

"Tell me about the minivan, Jane."

"The lineup is next week." She snips hair from my temple, her voice short and terse. I feel her hesitate, then she starts trimming again with quick hands. "If it's them, I'll get rid of the gun."

She says this offhandedly, a small step in my direction.

"I'll go with you," I say, the only concession I can think to have.

Her fingers hug my scalp, but she continues to cut, a focused professional with no space for dialogue, no room for error.

I want to tell her I've failed her. As she moves around my head until she is standing in front of me, scissors held above my forehead, I want to tell her I am sorry, for all my mistakes and theirs, the hospital's and the police and the faults of men. I will eat every single mistake until there are no more left, I will swallow them so she is safe, no guns and no minivans, no sidewalks and no darkness. But when I look up at her and she finally meets my eyes, there are no words for how the world has lost her.

Because there is nothing else, I reach my hand out to her chest.

Breastbone, I say.

She holds my eyes for a moment, then looks away when hers begin to brim.

So she can concentrate again and finish the haircut she's started, I tell her Toby asked about her today, to lighten this space and help us forget. She is so quiet I think maybe she hasn't heard me, but then she laughs a little and the sound spills through the bathroom, a sound like marbles, as though we are children again.

"Toby," Jane says. "I'll have to come see him soon."

When Jane finally completes the haircut, she stands back and observes my head. Her expression is the same as when she inspects her own scalp, like she's looking for the faults, the hairs that don't belong. But when her eyes move down and meet mine, her face softens, and for a moment we are who we've always been, a moment small as a seed, one to grow a world where we find the movements to begin again. ⬿

Bruise in the Shape of a Hand

Jehanne Dubrow

Her face, like one of those ancient caves where a man has left his signature. Handprint to say, I was here—this body made of stone belongs to me. My mother is made of stone. Before she steps outside, the man demands foundation the color of skin. Cover yourself, he says. His palm is everywhere, the little spots of swelling on her cheek, the wince and squint of it. How to hide the purple by the eye? The cut with powder? How to pencil in a pair of uncontusioned lips?

∞

Interview

Jehanne Dubrow

Can you describe the man in
question? Can you describe the
man? Between the hours of what
and what? Between what street
and where? Please indicate the
places on your body. Can you
turn left? Please face the other
way. Can you recall his face? Do
any of these faces look like his?
Look closely at each face. Do
any of these names? Name three
important features. What other
parts of him? Was it a rose? Was
it a rose with letters underneath?
What kind of ink? All black? Or
black with pink? What kind of
voice? Could you identify the
voice behind the glass? Can we go
back? How did he enter when he
entered? How did he go? Can we
go back to earlier? How did you
know the man? Can we go back?
Was there a lock? A key? What did
he ask? How many times? Please
say how many times. Can you
describe the man again? How tall
he was, how thin? Can you repeat
the question that he asked? Can
you repeat the question? Can you
repeat? Repeat it, please.

∞

Despondency

Jennifer Barber

Mild, persistent, low-grade,
a fever that doesn't spike,
it couches in me but would never

ask for my life or rush
through me with wild adrenalin,
hood me so that I couldn't see

my daughter's face, my husband's.
Instead it quietly robs
the savor from a day, ignores

the beauty of seven lemons
in a net bag, summer light
across a floorboard; it suspects

the worst of a friend,
tamps me down to a monotone
for hours, for weeks,

then turns to ask point-blank
why I've been holding back.
It believes in familiarity,

not planning, not imagining
the shapes that others pluck
from the precincts of new thought.

Now and then it departs
with no warning, the day
soaked in brightness, sheer as air.

෴

Moab

Jennifer Lee

When Jill Harrington and her mother arrived at our summer barbeque, I hid behind the picnic table. All afternoon, circling the grills where fathers flipped burgers, I kept her in sight. It was the week before we started first grade, and I hadn't seen her since the first days of June when we had gone swimming together at the municipal pool and celebrated the beginning of summer with ice cream cones. Adults were shocked to see her too, but they hid it better than I did.

"Don't stare." My mother whispered the words into the back of my neck. Her warm breath raised bumps across my shoulders, made the short hairs rise. But I couldn't stop. The red, pillowy scars on Jill's face were as fascinating as road kill or naked bodies. Her left cheek had melted and dripped down her neck and chest, and it was impossible to tell how much of her was burnt beneath the light, loose shirt she wore. Mrs. Harrington told my mother that the worst burns were there, under the shirt, and all through our first grade year I stared secretly at Jill, imagining a purple swelling beneath the cloth, raw, like a wound that had just lost its scab.

Riding to school next to Jill, the grainy texture of the plastic seat stuck to my thighs and left its mark of pressed red lines. I was afraid to meet her eye. I was afraid she would see my relief that this thing had happened to her and not me. But she never looked in my direction. She kept her face turned toward the window, and I stared straight ahead at the driver's rearview mirror. We were small enough and the seats were wide enough that our bodies never touched.

I hated Jill Harrington. I hated her for having pulled a pot of boiling water onto herself and changing everything. And I hated my mother and the other adults who acted like nothing was wrong.

We rode the bus together all of first grade, until my family moved to the outskirts of town and I changed schools. It was like a tray of bricks had been lifted from my chest. The air seemed lighter, fresher, the colors of the red rock mesas on the horizon more vivid. There was no one you had to pretend not to see.

Nearly forty years later I still live in Moab. Not really in town, but when strangers ask, they want to hear a name that is printed on their map. People come from all over the world to Moab. They come for the Arches, the Canyon Lands. They come for the Red Rock Country, sandstone buttes worn to needles, scoured thumbprints of geologic time. And all over that country, between the Parks and Moab, are houses like mine: one-story crumbling stucco, no porch, no tree for shade. My husband, Mike, hates that, that there is no tree. He says it makes him feel like trailer trash, as if our little house lacks the permanence only a tree can give it. I point out the humped rock fin behind the house, over thirty feet tall, how it gives us shade, anchors our home better than any tree. He doesn't see it that way.

In Mike's view, the next best thing to a house is a car. He bought us a red Chevy truck at the beginning of the summer, the same week the tumor was removed from my left breast. "Your tumor is the size and shape of a small chicken's egg," my doctor said, holding his thumb and forefinger in a loose oval. "Too small to warrant reconstruction." But when I touch myself there, something is missing, a hollowness beneath my fingers, barely visible in the mirror. It sickens me to touch it, but my fingers keep drifting there, like a child running her tongue over the salty gum of a lost tooth.

Riding with the boys in the hot cab, I draw the shoulder strap cautiously across my chest. Tim and Jason are ten and eight and think they're something else, riding around town in our new Chevy. What I want most is for summer to end, for Tim and Jason to go back to school. What the boys want is to ride into town everyday in our big red truck and spend the afternoon at the pool.

The municipal swimming pool is the same damp cinderblock construction I was wild about as a child, but there isn't any appeal left for me. Most of Moab is like this—a little run-down but essentially unchanged in the last fifty years. In some ways it's a comfort—the diner, the shops, the ice cream parlor, the pool—all just as they have always been. It is only the people who change.

The pool, of course, is the last place I want to be. I hadn't worried about buying a bathing suit or being naked in a locker room for over twenty years, but last week I spent four miserable hours at the department store trying on every suit they had. I brought home three to model for Mike. At first he smiled, flirting, thinking I was going to do a catwalk. But when I kept asking him the same questions—"Does it show? Can you see?"—he slumped in his chair and shook his head, saying over and over the same thing, "They all look fine, Honey. You can't tell at all."

It is nearly August when the boys finally get me into the pool. They've been dunking each other for about an hour when Tim shouts, "Mom! Mom, get in!"

"No," I say. I'm sitting in the shade with a book.

"You never get in with us," Jason cries. He is eight and speaks in superlatives: never, always, everything.

"Look, that mom is swimming with her kid." Tim is sly; he knows what arguments might move me. The boys are crouched in the water at the edge of the pool and have begun splashing my feet. This game can only move in one direction.

"Okay, but I'm keeping my hat and my sunglasses on. No rough stuff."

Last year I would have cannonballed into the water with them, and here I am walking primly down the steps into the shallow end. Once in the four-foot side, I bend at the knees until my chin touches the water, and I start paddling over the concrete floor. Each of my boys clings to a shoulder, their pink seal bodies stretched out on the water, legs gently kicking to keep from sinking. They hold on so gently, so carefully, that it seems they are keeping me afloat rather than the other way around.

In front of us a woman plays with her son. She is enormous, over 300 pounds, and I figure she likes the water for the relief it gives her from carrying all that weight. Her boy is older than mine, twelve, maybe even thirteen. He climbs fiercely on his mother's shoulders, trying to dunk her. She laughs, dunking him instead. I wonder how much longer they have to play together like this, before the boy outgrows it.

Jason rotates his body until his face is in front of mine. I can smell peanut butter on his breath. "You're prettier than her," he says.

Before Mike and I got married, when I was still waiting tables at Hot Rocks, I passed for one of the prettiest girls in town. Local boys and the hiker types left big tips, hoping I'd go for a ride with them after the bar closed. Mike was one of those. He was never a big spender, but then he didn't give up easily either. He came in the bar often that first year he was in town. He had followed a construction job from Grand Junction where he'd grown up and then stuck around. We started going out after a while. He liked that I knew where the hot springs were, knew the best places to watch the sun set with a bottle of wine. It didn't feel like love at first— we were just having good times. But once when we were hiking Devil's Garden—it was off-season, and we were alone on the most spectacular hike in the Arches—he asked me, "What do you want to be like when you're old?"

I'd thought of this before, many times. Age is something easy to think about in Red Rock Country. I ran my hand along the rough texture of stone, warm from the sun and carved by wind. "Like this," I said. "I want to be like this when I'm old."

Mike looked over the rocks and sand and sparse native grass. He nodded. "This country ages well. I suppose that's what we all want."

We carried a blanket with us. Stretched over the warm sandstone, that nubby old rag was better than any bed. We climbed high up a rock fin, a broad one that towered thirty feet in the air. Flat as a table on top, we could have jogged in circles if we liked. Lying down, no one on the ground could see us.

Mike and I found lots of those places, all the country open before us, and we would stretch out on the blanket, make love under the sun, feel the earth spin with our weightlessness.

Twenty years later he looks the same to me. His hair is thinner, but still dark, and the lines on his face are deeper, but there are no new ones. Or else I don't see them. His body is the same, that's for sure. A working man's body—thickly muscled with a permanent tan. The dark hairs on his forearms set off his complexion, and women watch him when he enters a room. I used to enjoy the way women looked at him. It was pride in the body, both mine and his. But I'm thinning out in ways that only I know. The removal of the tumor, yes, but also a strange papery-ness that has come over my skin, as though it is slipping away from the muscle and fat beneath. I follow Mike across the crowded floors of restaurants, the eyes of women on him, and feel that only part of me is present. Something important has drained away like sand.

I kiss Jason's nose and slowly spin his floating body so that I am no longer looking at the woman and her son playing near us in the pool.

"What should we do? Think of a game we can play where I won't have to put my head under."

"Spider!" Tim lets go of me and swims toward the far side of the pool. The boys love this game, slipping through the gaps I make by bracing my limbs across a corner in the deep end. My feet are spread against the rough texture of the wall, and my hands are far apart, gripping the curved lip of the pool's edge. The boys take turns sliding in and out of my web. Jason goes first, and his back and legs bob like corks against my arm, his slick smooth skin tingling against mine. Facing me in the corner he pushes the hair off his forehead and blinks his eyes, red and watery from the chlorine.

"Did I touch you?" he asks.

"No," I tell him, "you made it."

"I thought I touched you."

I shake my head. "I didn't feel a thing."

Jason takes a deep, triumphant breath and plunges down between my legs. This time all I feel is the swirl of water as he vanishes.

Tim has more strategy than his brother. He takes half breaths so he won't float as much and moves slowly, gripping the wall to be sure. He doesn't touch me, but if he had I would have called him on it without mercy. Anything less would infuriate him.

We play several rounds, the boys alternating their path in and out of the web. After twenty minutes I am tired of the game.

"Okay, guys, last time."

Jason pops up between my legs and pouts. "How come we always have to leave early?"

"Because I have the keys to the car. Come on. I'll buy you ice cream."

Tim and Jason haul their wet, rubbery selves out of the water and speed-walk toward the locker room, their round butts pivoting madly as they try to keep to the no-running rule and still get ice cream as quick as possible. They will be grouchy and annoyed by the time I emerge on the other side of the locker room twenty minutes later. It is always the same, but it never slows them down any.

I take my time crossing the concrete deck, gathering up bags and books and towels and clutching them to my chest like camouflage. Whoever designed the layout of the pool house lacked a modest turn of mind. In the women's room only one shower has a curtain, and the changing area consists of a long bench beneath a row of hooks on the wall. There are two changing stalls with latched wooden doors, but self-conscious ten-year-olds usually commandeer them.

At this hour mostly older women—grandmothers looking after toddlers while the parents work—occupy the changing room. We shower with our suits on and turn our backs on one another when dressing.

The transition from light to dark leaves me temporarily blind. Around me, though, I hear more people than I expect. The showers blast full force, a white-noise background to a chorus of German voices ringing off the walls. My heart sinks, knowing what I will see. Youthful campers who come to Moab for the sole purpose of hiking descend on the municipal swimming pool to take their showers. Most travel in groups of three or four, but sometimes a large group arrives, usually Europeans, and now it feels like the entire population of twenty-year-olds from some small Bavarian town has come to Moab on holiday. As my eyes adjust to the gloom of the bath house, I see a horde of lithe blond girls swarming like locusts around the showers and benches and mirrors.

They move about like Valkyries, naked in the steam. I try to look away, keep my eyes on the floor like the old women, but I can't. I stare about like the smallest child.

At first all the girls seem perfect, the way twenty-year-olds do. Some are all long skinny limbs, some have a solid swarthiness, but all of them are beautiful. I take my turn under the last shower in the row, rub liquid soap into the loose pelt of my bathing suit. Under the water's curtain I look more closely at the girl next to me. Even wet her short hair doesn't reach below her ears. She tilts her face into the stream of water, eyes closed. The heat of the water raises small red marks in her skin, old scars about her mouth and nose and eyes. They are shaped like tear drops. Larger scars mark her neck and shoulders. Below, her chest is unscathed, her torso a brilliant white up to where it meets her sunburned limbs. She opens her eyes and sees me staring.

"It was a dog."

"Excuse me?"

"When I was very small a dog bit me many times. See? On my face is the most, but the doctor did a good job. They are small now, the scars."

"I'm sorry. I didn't mean to stare." I am grateful for the water between us, for the heat that might explain the scarlet blush I feel.

"It's okay, really." She smiles, revealing a crooked tooth, and turns off her shower. I stand there in my dripping suit and watch her move away.

The row of showers is empty except for me, and I listen to the relaxing sound of water draining beneath the concrete floor. I feel the pinch of my bathing suit straps, the tight elastic on my thighs. The material seems to hold more and more water, dragging me down. I peel the suit from my shoulders and let it slide to the floor with a wet slap.

Alone in the shower with the rushing water and the billowing steam, I stare wondering at the long valley between my breasts, the low hill of my abdomen run with stretch marks like tracks of erosion. In the corner of my eye I can see the welt of scar, the slight dish in the flesh of my left breast. I squirt liquid soap into my hand and begin to wash. My hands slide over my skin, loose on muscle and bone, over and over until my body feels familiar. Children watch me wash, grandmothers too. I don't care.

I dry myself slowly and wrap a towel around my waist. I join the German girls at the mirrors and balance my bag of lotions on the porcelain lip of the sink. On my left stands the girl from the shower, gel spiking up her short hair, an eyeliner in her hand. I rub moisturizer into my skin, trying to beat back the desert wrinkles as best I can when our eyes meet in the mirror. Her eyes remind me of Jason's: startlingly clear and seductive. She smiles slightly, revealing again the crooked tooth. I can't take my eyes from her.

In the cooler air her scars have faded. If I hadn't seen them flushed in the shower, streaking her face like a child's drawing of rain, I would have taken them for the mundane reminder of a bad case of chicken pox. Her eyes travel the glass, searching for something in me. Naked to the waist, it doesn't take her long to find the scar on my breast. She looks back at my eyes, expectant, a small smile playing at her lips.

"It was a tumor," I tell her. "They took it out in June. It was the size of an egg." I hold up my thumb and forefinger in a round O for emphasis. She nods, still smiling, and I see her blue eye through the circle of my fingers before she turns to leave.

Outside in the sun the boys are as grouchy as I'd predicted. They scowl and kick loose stones on the sidewalk. I smile vacantly, still thinking of the beautiful, scarred girl in the shower. Perhaps somewhere Jill Harrington too can smile in the mirror at a stranger. We walk the four blocks to the ice cream shop, passing in and out of shade.

An old bell on a trip wire rings when Tim pushes the door open; it's a sound I've known all my life. Jill and I once stood before the cold glass and drew hearts in the steam of our mingled breath. Our bodies touched as we made our choices. The flavors haven't changed; there is still Rocky Road and Rainbow Swirl, Jill's favorite and mine. There are some things you can choose and some you can't.

My boys lean into the frigid glass and point to their flavors. I let them order double scoops, which later drip in melting streams as we walk back down the street. ∞

Crayons

Emily Sullivan Sanford

Every spring I must explain my arms to children,
before my legs arrive in summer.

The scars hold their eyes.
I can draw scars,
bright purple or beige.

Leave my arm on the edge, the ledge,
not to fall over but to absorb
some print of danger,
of the almost.

The adults hold the almost question:
What did happen?

I drew scars for myself.
No accidents anywhere.

Children reach out their arms, beg.
"I want to touch your scars again."

Eyes are not enough for drawing.

&

Stage Four, Summer

Pat Daneman

Because she liked the colors of vegetables,
she cooked. And every day she rode her bike
around the ball field, though by August

only around the block—and she knew,
as she snapped the padlock shut,
that the last day was the last day.

She baked zucchini bread and read magazines
and cooked eggplant and tomatoes, green beans
and summer squash. She walked out for the mail,

drank tea, and learned things her doctors didn't know—
how the bedroom carpet felt against her cheek,
how with the telephone not ringing, music

could climb hills inside her head, color them
bright green as with a child's hand.
Backwards and forwards she learned the alphabet

of her dreams and how to dream
with eyes open. Day and night she watched
the sky. She thought about autumn coming—her bones

rattling against her clothes, bald pumpkins
scattered like teeth in the fields,
as gardens everywhere died.

∽

Hamlet

Benjamin Parzybok

Hamlet was in the basement bottling beer when the phone calls began. Every ten minutes or so the answering machine wound up his voice, which sounded more tired in each incarnation, beeped, and took the new message from his brother.

Ring. "Ham, you got to pick up here, okay? This is your last chance to—what am I saying? It's really beyond that. At least make it right in your mind."

Hamlet washed the bottle caps and surveyed his apparatus. He began an internal countdown to the next phone call. He could hear the drink in his brother's voice, and felt a certain synchronicity there.

Ring. "Ham, this is Ed again. Bro? Are you there?"

Ring. "Ham, I know you're there. I'll buy your ticket. Come to the funeral, shake a few hands, head home. It's not just about you—think of all the aunts and uncles."

Hamlet sat on the laundry hamper and took a pull off a bottle of beer not yet capped. The taste was overly hoppy, too carbonated, sediment-rich and, if he were to admit it, downright awful. It was the taste of beer not yet left to age. But it was the taste of *his* beer, and so there was pride wrapped up in it. It was the taste of wealth, of sorts. If, like last winter, he couldn't afford to heat his house the season through, he'd still have this stash. It would taste better then, but for now it had alcohol and in the end that was what mattered. As far as he was concerned the rest was just window dressing.

Drinking was going to help. That had been his plan the moment his brother's brassy voice spilled from the answering machine into his cold house some hours before. Their mother had died early that morning. He hadn't spoken to her in ten years.

Ring. "Ham? Jesus Christ."

"Hamlet," he said to himself. Hating the name. The name that she had given him. And why? Perhaps because when he'd brazenly entered the world dressed in the wrong gender she decided to punish him, to seal some tragicomic fate clear only in her mind. Or perhaps she thought she'd force-inject some class into a family surviving on a car salesman's wages. Perhaps she knew far in advance that he would stand with his father on the wrong side of her desires. And when his father died, she turned her marital war on the next most-likely subject.

When he tried to recall a line of her dialogue, it came to him in the perfect tenor of her voice. "The way you do one thing is the way you do all things."

It was a blanket condemnation. She'd said it about the eye injury that got him out of the Vietnam War; she'd said it about his marriage and his wife's boyfriends; she'd said it about his kids' school clothes, his working-class pursuits, his inability to climb any kind of corporate or social ladder, his continual forsaking of established jobs in favor of independence, even at the price of poverty.

Ring. "Ham Ham Ham…" His brother sighed, breathed into the phone for a few moments.

"Fucking mama's boy," Hamlet said.

"The way—"

"If you say it," he growled. "If you say it—"

"—the way to become her, goddamnit, is to block her out…" Hamlet sprinted up the basement stairs. "Listen, I've got a friend who's a—"

"Shut up shut up shut up," he yelled. He yanked the phone from the desk and it sent the answering machine underneath spinning until its trajectory was brought to an abrupt halt by the cord that tethered it to the phone jack. His brother's voice continued.

"…and I think he could really help you. Nobody denies that she was a—"

Hamlet grabbed each side of the answering machine and wrenched it from its socket on the wall. The room filled up with quiet.

On inspection, he realized that he'd destroyed the answering machine phone jack. Hamlet sat on the bed and put his head in his hands. "The way you do one thing…"

He fetched some Elmer's glue from the kitchen catchall drawer and sat at the table trying to repair what he could of the phone jack. A new answering machine would be $25, minimum. The glue was difficult to work with at this scale and a couple of drops began to coagulate on the table. "Fuck me," he said and pushed the unfinished repair job into the center of the table.

He stared out the window where a dusting of snow came down whitely among the trees. From a corner of the sky a hazy moon put a dim glow on things. A frustration so overwhelming it brought a flush of tears to his eyes racked through him and then was gone. For a brief moment he let himself consider going to the funeral, seeing all his mother's sisters, his uncles, trying to face down the stares directed at someone who spent the last decade of his mother's life in a grudge match.

Hamlet opened the fridge, swaying within the emotional vacuum that ripping the phone out of the wall had created. He had set up his life in opposition to her, and without her tying him fast he felt unmoored, drifting about for portage. There was one beer left in the fridge. Then he remembered the operation downstairs.

The bottling was going well. Twenty-five gallons of beer. In an operation of this size an efficient system was imperative. At the beginning he felt himself correct minutely to save effort with every few bottles, and the system got tighter with each iteration. He siphoned nine bottles at a time, kinked the hose, wiped the tops, placed the caps, cranked down on the bottler, boxed them and put the case on the shelf. It was an exhausting job to do alone and he'd developed a blister in the sag of skin between his thumb and forefinger, but it was the growing wall of beer cases that kept him humming through the work. By case fourteen, though, his head ached and his hands felt arthritic. He felt the system unraveling as he grew progressively drunker.

With the sixteenth box bottled up, he stood up from his stool and wondered if perhaps something wasn't quite right with the beer. The washing machine appeared to him as a stop-motion slide show, as though he were the one spinning and blinking. There was the sound of a click from somewhere and Hamlet started. It was a bottle settling, perhaps, or a small item dropping, but with his mother dead there was a spookiness to the basement he hadn't felt before. He looked toward the darkened end of the basement where it turned into a dirt crawl space and shuddered. Were his mother to take up haunting he couldn't imagine a more likely place or person to haunt. He leaned down and picked the box of nine bottles up and felt the burning in his stomach that meant he would need another operation for his hiatal hernia. He staggered the box over to the shelves and hoisted it to the top of the stack there, well over his head.

It could have been anything—that his hands were sore, that a bottle shifted, that the floor was covered in a thin veneer of beer. It could have been from thinking about the funeral. Or perhaps it was the weight of another cold winter descending, of fretting at the grocery store shelves, of sleeping in his jacket under the covers. Whatever the case, Hamlet lost control of the box as he stood on his toes. It teetered at the tips of his fingers for an instant, his motion slowed, his dexterity like a winter bear's. The box tipped then and bottles slipped independently from their cardboard silos, one after the other colliding with his head or shoulders or back, each following its own path to destruction, careening heavily down to the floor, as did he.

He awoke groggily and became aware of the coldness of the concrete across his body, his hands numb. From his vantage he looked out across the basement floor and could not remember the place. It was not the efficient home brewer's operation he'd imagined, but the mad pursuit of a lonely man in his basement. Glass glittered about him on the floor in a sea of beer foam and blood. He picked himself up, his hand wet and red where it had tenderly touched the top of his head; shards of glass were embedded in his cheek. The house was cold and empty above him, and it was not lost on him that had he not regained consciousness his body would have lain undiscovered for a great long time.

Upstairs he inspected the gash through the thinning hair there and tried to measure if it warranted a trip to the emergency room that he could not afford. He stripped and took a shower tentatively, barely managing to wash the wound on his head for the pain. He watched his blood dilute to pink in the water. His mother had been disgusted by the show of pain in others, especially by men.

He piled blankets over himself and watched the ten o'clock news and felt sorry for himself. Every few minutes a drop of blood would make it through his saturated make-shift bandage and follow the rivulet down his forehead, along the inside of his nose and, were he to let it, into his mouth. He kept a handkerchief there and dabbed at each one as it fell. He would have been happy to relax into the chair and let the TV rumble through the night. Outside the sky glowed darkly with no particular point of light or definition.

He wondered if his brother had continued to call into his dead line, or if his mother's ghost circled around in the basement below, waiting for him to return.

In the middle of a feel-good broadcast about a pet-shop owner, Hamlet woke with the taste of the blood that had pooled at the corner of his mouth while he dozed off. He swore and unraveled himself from his blankets. In the garage he rummaged through his hand-carved boxes for one that looked expensive. He donned his boots and jacket and toyed fretfully with the idea of a hat until he settled on a towel turban wrapped tightly around his head. He opened his door and went into the icy haze.

Outside, the silence was absolute. The snow was fine and fog-like, obscuring the street signs and anything farther than twenty feet. He weaved a little and felt himself growing faint as he passed his neighbor's house. The clinic was four blocks up and eight blocks over, nearly the distance of the small town. The houses he passed glowed warmly and he smelled smoke and snow in the air. He felt a drop of blood make its way from under the towel and realized he must have soaked it now, too. He felt glad for the snow; in it there was concealment. He tried not to think of his mother out there, separated from what kept her anchored to the earth and in one place, out there as part of some all-knowing, all-seeing whatever that he very much hoped did not exist.

On the corner of Fifth and Main, Hamlet stumbled and the ice quickly took him to his hands and knees. He paused there, transfixed, as drops of blood bore a black hole into the snow. With great effort he set himself on his way again.

At the emergency clinic there was a car accident ahead of him. The father of a teenage girl who'd bunged up her nose when her car drifted into a telephone pole read *US News & World Report* and studiously avoided looking at him, dressed as he was like a terrorist fresh from a car bombing or a bath. Hamlet stared at his hands and fidgeted with his blister. He felt a fleeting and confused regret that he had asked his mother to strike him from her will, in an effort to snip the puppet strings.

The nurse practitioner's name was Nancy. She was roughly his age and actually took his hand to lead him back to a room for inspection. She bustled along energetically, walking him faster than he was used to. Her hands were warm and meaty and she glowed with a welcoming friendliness.

"Well, you look like you've had a rough night."

"Yes, ma'am," Hamlet said, "I was bottling up some homemade beer and the bottles got rough on me."

"Is that so?" she said. She talked animatedly, so that as she spoke, her hair, with its few remaining strands of brown in the sea of gray, danced about her cheeks.

"The greatest tragedy is, I lost a case," he said.

"I think you're just supposed to drink the stuff—or am I wrong here?"

"No, no," Hamlet said. "Beer goes straight to my head."

Nancy smiled at him and though he was dizzy and hurt he wondered what he could do to make her smile again.

"Hamlet," she said. "Didn't he poison Ophelia?" She winked as she pushed him into a chair in a close room.

"No—he drove her mad. You heard how he talks? And then she drowned herself."

"Oh ho!" She leaned in to inspect his head. He could smell her warmth, her flesh pressed against him.

"Gertrude—that's Hamlet's mother—was really opposite to my own mother. I'm not sure what she intended when she named me," he said, and then wondered if he'd just said too much.

"I'm going to have to give you a few stitches here it looks like. Going to need to shave an area here as well."

"Yeah, well, that seems to be the direction of things."

"It'll give you a youthful look, we'll send you away with a skateboard," she said.

"Listen," he said, hating that he had to ruin the rapport with what came next. He backed away so he could look her in the eyes. "I have a gift for you."

Nancy put her hand to her chest and he saw a wariness in the expression. He dug around in his coat for the box; it was bone cold to the touch. He held it out with two hands toward her and watched as her expression changed from wariness to interest and then to wary restraint again.

"But what for…? It's very pretty."

"Thank you, I made it," he sighed. It depressed him that they had to have this detour. "The thing is," he started. His face felt like all the blood had drained from it and he was dizzy and perhaps a little drunk still. "I was hoping we could…" He couldn't bring himself to say the word trade, his throat making things difficult, clamping down on the word. Nancy took a barely perceptible step backward. "I was hoping we could…" He set the box in his lap and with both pointer fingers gestured rapidly back and forth between Nancy and himself.

"Oh?" she said.

He saw that she misunderstood. "I mean for the stitches. I'm really sorry, I don't have any…any money."

"Oh honey, listen, I would love to, but… Of course I will, but unless you've got another box in there I'm going to need to talk to the front desk."

"No, no I'm sorry. Forget it—" He began to stand.

"Wait. Stop." She held up her hand dramatically, like a school crossing guard. "You just wait right here."

While she was gone he worked on his breathing, trying to overcome that morning-after feeling of shame, that feeling of having all your goods out on the table. He studied a poster on Sexually Transmitted Diseases and admired the young Latina that was the spokesperson or something.

She bumped back into the room and smiled; he could see she was enjoying this, that she was going to make it easy. "Alright, let's have a look-see at that box." She took it into her hands and inspected it. "It's just lovely—you're very talented. Are these runes?" She looked up at him between strands of hair that had slipped in front of her eyes.

"Yes. Magic. Spells." He smiled.

"Wow. And what do they do? Bend one's will to my bidding, I hope."

"It's a spell to heal a head wound. Circuitously, it turns out."

"Oh ho! Touché. The patient thinks he may die here. Yes, we better get you stitched up before you go fainting on me." She winked again but the flirt was over for him and he bent his head somberly so that she could get to work.

It stung like hell, and that made him feel better. He stared at her waist and hips. He wanted to reach out and hug her big leg to his chest. The snow fell outside and covered everything up. His tracks here would be whitewashed back into the fabric, the whole town cocooned under the blanket.

When she finished he felt drained of blood and exhausted, but he managed to resuscitate the obligatory charm that he knew was required when you arrived at a place without money, and he could tell she appreciated it. She joked back ably as he back-stepped his way out the door.

Outside he stood for a moment and let snow fall on his face. Perhaps he should have taken the offered juice to prevent blood sugar collapse, after all.

He stood on the corner for a moment gathering himself and then he saw her across the intersection. She was dressed in beige. A beige pantsuit. Her hair—a blond-beige—was done up elegantly. His mother stared at him. A shudder took root in his spine so that he could not stop shaking. He didn't know what to do. Self-consciously he raised his arm and waved, but there was no reaction from her.

Her feet disappeared into the snow and he wondered if she were cold. There was only a single pair of tracks in the snow—his from earlier, a blanket of white softening their edges. She stood in them on her side of the road; she had been stepping in each of his footprints.

"Mother," he called, "Please. Please don't." He bowed his head and wasn't sure what he was asking her. Please forgive him, please leave him alone, please give him one last chance, please see him safely home. He could not bring himself to cross the street.

After a while she took off a boot and shook the snow out of it while standing on one foot. He wanted to keep walking, walking in some other direction, but his legs were so heavy and each step had felt as if he were dealt a bible blow to the crown of his head.

"Mother?" he called, and the voice was that of a little boy. He wondered if he ought to tell her he was sorry but realized he wouldn't mean it. No—he wanted an apology from *her*. For riding his father into the grave, for riding him, on the back of him until he teetered over the edge of the world. He did not want to cross the street. He stood and stared back, feeling himself become the person he most hated—tensed and ready to defend. Small and wary under her omniscient, critical eye.

She took off her other boot and shook out the snow and along with the snow something tumbled to the ground there.

"Hey, Hamlet," a voice close to him called.

He looked down from the apparition to see that a car had pulled in front of him.

"You didn't tell me you were on foot," Nancy said. "Get in here, I can't let you go wandering off on a night like this, not when you might be concussed. Where do you live?"

He said no, he'd prefer to walk and kept his eyes focused on the spot where his mother was. A great gust of snow blew through the intersection that separated them and when it lessened she was gone. He looked down and was surprised to see the car still there. He opened the door and sat down heavily. The car was warm and the lighted cockpit against the backdrop of dark snow reassured him.

"I dropped my..." he trailed off and pointed across the street. He was having trouble holding his hand up.

"Oh, hon," Nancy said. She jumped out of the car and loped across the street to where his footprints remained. She returned with a handful of change. "Is this what you dropped?"

He counted: five quarters, three dimes, and two nickels. Every one of them minted in 1951, the year of his birth.

On the way to his house he found himself dizzily loquacious, saying that his heat was off and that he lived alone, and he barely recognized the person who might say such things. Hamlet watched for his mother out the passenger window, his head resting against the glass. Was it bus fare? He couldn't think what else a dollar sixty-five could buy.

Each windy swirl of snow created a shimmering outline of a ghostly figure and then the illusion drifted apart. It didn't feel like familiar territory any more; the car had gone past his house.

"I've got a great couch," Nancy was saying. "With your concussion you need someone checking on you every four hours." He tried to protest, but the car was warm and his body suddenly talked out.

She flicked on her turn signal. "You allergic to cats?"

Later in the night Nancy appeared in front of him in something sheer. She asked about his head, did he still remember who was president, what his name was.

"Hamlet," he managed to croak out. He couldn't understand what the purpose of the questions were, and even when they were done she seemed to linger there.

"You're cold," he heard her say.

Look at how fat she is, he thought in a voice that felt like his mother's. He heard her there, the bitter resonance of her on his tongue. He tried to think of the best way to say no while knowing he had never had the social graces not to offend, and then he found himself standing, and she was leading him by the hand, her dressing gown floating ghost-like in front of him. She led him into her bedroom, lit by the soft glow of a bedside lamp. There were great heaps of books everywhere—the floor a treacherous mass of them, shelves warped under their weight. An indented corner of the bed was thick with hair, as if a cat had long ago decomposed there, the blanket's memory of it all that was left.

"No," he said. His voice warbled and hesitant and sudden in the room.

"I should have put you here in the first place. I'll be on the couch, hon."

He was unsteady, his feet cantilevered across a carpet of novels.

"You lie down," she whispered and helped him into her bed. "You just lie there."

On the bedside table he saw a younger-version photo of her standing alone in front of the Eiffel Tower. The girl in the photo wore a skirt, the hem raised above one knee from the angle of her hips, and she smiled with an easy wryness, indulgent in whomever fidgeted with the camera. He wondered with a touch of envy who had wielded it. Perhaps the photo had been put there to remind herself of other, grander possibilities, or perhaps it was only her daughter.

Nancy did not let go of his hand as he leaned his head back onto the pillow, or he did not let go of hers, clutching it as he was lowered into a well of unconsciousness. She turned off the light and he closed his eyes with the darkness and he could hear her there in the room, connected to him by fingers that he gripped to keep from falling off the edge of the world.

"Hmm," she said, and gave her captive hand a futile, playful shake. And then she slipped into bed beside, scooted close, and folded a leg across his.

In the morning he awoke with a headache, a pounding conspiracy between injury and alcohol, worsened by the sudden realization he was not at home. He studied the woman sleeping next to him. Her mouth was fleshy and parted and she breathed heavily. Out the window he saw that the snow still fell, but there was a lightening, they had gone through the worst of it. Her hair, which smelled nice, framed her face just so. She closed her lips. The rhythm of her breathing softened. Her cheeks were flushed and her eyebrows were dark and expressive. At the corner of one eye was the smallest of moles, or perhaps it was only a freckle, a suggestion of exoticness.

Then her eyes were open and she'd seen him studying her. He wanted to look away but in those eyes there was a gale storm of energy and what came beaming out of them forced him to keep his eyes steady.

"Hiya, Hamlet," she said, smiling. "How's your head?"

The name turned him cold. He wanted to roll away from that ugly face and get out of there, get the hell out of this house.

His head ached and he'd awoken in a foreign place, a foreign body beside him, bus fare in his jeans pocket. His head ached and he was being haunted. He sensed her out there, beyond the door, applying eye shadow in the bathroom, finding expired foodstuffs in the refrigerator, dusting behind the couch.

Then an idea surfaced from somewhere inside him, like an air bubble rising from a deep lake. The idea turned and twisted about, putting pressure against his insides until it bubbled out of him.

"I'm changing my name," he said. Just saying it out loud made him feel different, like some thickened skin had been pulled back to reveal the fruit underneath, like maybe it wasn't too late. "I'm changing my name."

Nancy smiled uncertainly. "You said that."

"I'm not sure to what."

"Can I help pick?" she said.

"Yes," he said. "Yes, anything you want."

"Hmmm," she said. She put her arms around and rolled into him, pulled him against her and he felt as if parts of him were falling off, as if his exo-skeleton had broken, and he saw that she was beautiful and he was dizzy and he could not remember his name. ဆ

The Bird Buriers

Ben Miller

Again I come to it—the dirt
upset by an old purse fork.

Me, the digger. Mother, she
petting failed feathers, adult

wren wrapped in a napkin,
freezer bag, any nearest litter.

Gray gritty clods. The dark
cakes marbled butterscotch.

There were rules as I recall.
Some made by us, some not.

Bird must be interred close
as possible to landing spot,

often a tough strip of turf
between sidewalk and curb.

Bird must be found when I
was already tardy to school.

After burial and prayer—we
must together look up, silent,

caring about nothing but
why wings fell from the sky.

೮౧

The Mortician's *Guayabera*

Virgil Suárez

It hangs behind the door, white like his hands,
after so much washing of bodies, flesh of pure

rapture. In the eyes of a dead child, a river
speaks of valleys, mountains, a scarf adrift

in the currents. In a dead man's mouth, a gift
of red words, a column of fire rising from cane

fields in the night. This man could be a father,
a son, or the Trinity. A scar runs down his spine

toward the back of his left leg, a sienna canyon
caught between two cupped hands of earth.

It is a bird, this shirt of white, tropical humidity,
mist rising above palm fronds in *el campo*, a *guajiro's*

garb, his suave style, ready for *decimas*, dance,
in the company of *campesina* ladies, white bird,

egret, stork, a dove, rising there behind the door.
You would not know of its longing, its passing.

In the night, when this man too used to silence,
wears it out in the cool evening breeze, it glows,

it comes alive. It is beacon of all those dying
for their return home. And if you return home,

you will wear the plumage of birds on your back,
the color of brackish water in your eyes, salt or sugar

in your mouth, the sting of tears from such radiance.

&

Sisters of Mercy

Joan Leegant

The surgeon came into the O.R. chewing gum. This was how we knew there'd be a problem. It wasn't the gum but what it was meant to disguise. We're not talking bad breath.

The patient was shaved, supine, out. His wife was in the plastic chair in the hall gripping the handle of her pocketbook. He's the best in the business, we assured her. Why don't you go home and wait there? Much more comfortable, your own living room, you could rent a movie, read a book. A tough bird, South Boston, she said she'd stay here thank you very much. You didn't leave your husband of forty-two years with a brain hemorrhage to go home and watch *Law & Order*.

Gloved, gowned, masked; we dressed him. A star in medical school. No rich parents putting him through. He was one of us. West Roxbury, Roslindale, Revere. Like the man on the table. Like all our brothers. He'd gone to school with our cousins, his parents went to Saint Anne's with ours, at sixteen he got into trouble for setting off Roman candles at Wollaston Beach. Girls like us have always been there to keep him in line. Mothers did it too. Aunts.

A twinkle in those baby blues as he winked at us—always a looker, which explained the three divorces—then turned his attention to the sufferer on the table. We'd all loved boys like him once, though they ignored us and went for the fast beauties, the bottle blondes with thick eyeliner and white lipstick who later landed real prizes and live in baronial splendor in Chestnut Hill with out-of-towners who made it in real estate and want them to work on the accent. Eliza Doolittles. They come in here and we know them beneath the designer jeans and corrected pronunciation. Sometimes they weep and want us to clasp them to our pastel bosoms and talk about the old neighborhood.

He's got the gleaming blade in his hand. God have mercy, we mutter under our breaths, as the boy genius peers down from his place at the head of the table, wielding the tiny saw like a father at Thanksgiving. We're saying Grace, we always do, because humans are fallible, some more fallible than others.

The hand begins to lower. Abraham at the altar, though where is the ram? One of us gently touches his wrist as another points to the thick black X made with a Sharpie an hour ago on the other side of the skull and murmurs *Over there, Doctor, not here.* He pauses, stops chewing, the faint scent behind the mask unmistakable, and glances up at us, only his ocean eyes showing, beseeching—*it was just this once, just today, I promise, please*—his sisters by proxy, we've been saving boys like him our whole lives. A barely perceptible nod as he shifts position, his jaw still, lowers the knife—steady as the best of them—and begins. ∞

My Hypochondria: A Soliloquy

Steve Gehrke

All day I felt a small disc of numbness just below
my scalp, a collapsed vein, I was sure, or a clot,

the first signs of a seizure coming on, of an aneurism,
or possibly a stroke, that anesthetized zero flaring

and disappearing for hours, like the red-blank-red
blinking of a stoplight, so that I lay awake that night

contemplating all the false scenarios of death: the helium
ascensions, the eternal returns, the crumbed body

called back into the grass, the unity, the whispering cup
on the Ouija board, but I found inside of me no heaven,

no Elysium, no Valhalla, no dreamtime, no Egyptian
Fields of Aaru, no meadow fat with buffalo, just the perfume

of myths, a bad disguise, like someone trying to cover
a bald spot, but the hole shows through, doesn't it, the numb-

spot at the center of the world, the straight-nothing that isn't
even black, which is what I felt leached to the top of my skull,

that yarmulke of emptiness, that blood-nothing at the core of us,
striking its one note for eternity, while our hearts, pink

and motherless, look to the sky with their eyes gummed shut,

like a nest of infant birds. When did I become
like this: paranoid, delusional? When did I start

looking at my own thoughts through a wall of glass?
When did I become this diminutive person, this toy man,

this Godless Pinocchio? Why can't I find the crack, gap,
that moment when the tape was spliced, that step in time

when the old self lifted a foot and the new one put it down?
Aren't there origins: the garden, the bang? Walk back against

the current, and won't you find the river's source?
Trace the etymology of every word and won't you find them

gathered in the same mouth, the same grunt, the same breath
across startled vocal chords? When did it begin, when was

that first drop of consciousness replaced? When did it start,
this abduction, this swap, this backwards dialysis of selves,

every molecule in my body muddied and returned? Why not hunt
the ghost of my former life? Why not hunt what haunts me? And if

the mind holds experience the way a Doppler holds weather—
as a symbol, as a code—then what choice is there except to chase

the storm back across the continents until the last ice-crystal
of cloud melts back into the oxygen, until the mind, bleached

and purified, reveals the noble blue that lies dormant within you,
or so that at least you can see that once you were okay,

that you were blameless, that you were luminous.

છ

Book Review

The Sound of a Wild Snail Eating

Elisabeth Tova Bailey

(Algonquin Books of Chapel Hill, 2010, 190 pages)

Reviewed by Jack Coulehan

Life inches forward very slowly for a person incapacitated by chronic, devastating illness. As Emily Dickinson wrote, "The velocity of the ill… is like that of a snail." In *The Sound of a Wild Snail Eating*, Elisabeth Tova Bailey describes being confined to bed for months in a single room of a borrowed apartment, her mind intact, but her body so weak, her autonomic nervous system so dysfunctional, that she couldn't even sit up in bed. Time slowed almost to a stop. Time accumulated in her solitary room, but she was unable to spend it. When friends visited, they moved quickly, always short on time. "My friends had so little time," she recalls, "I often wished I could give them what time I could not use."

Bailey describes how one day a visitor brought her a pot of violets, and among the violets was a small snail she had picked up in the woods. Later that night Bailey noticed a sound like "someone very small munching celery continuously." In the quiet room, she could actually hear the sound of a snail eating! Initially, it chewed tiny holes in her writing paper. But shortly after receiving the little mollusk, Bailey acquired a glass terrarium, which her caregiver filled with ferns, moss, and other native plants to provide the snail with a rich natural environment. During nighttime hours when her sleep was "diaphanous or nonexistent," she began carefully to observe the nocturnal creature as it went about its activities. "Its companionship was a comfort to me," she writes, "and buffered my feelings of uselessness."

The Sound of a Wild Snail Eating is a meditation on the relationship between a woman and a woodland snail. Bailey's illness, a mysterious condition called chronic fatigue syndrome, held her captive, severing most connections to her former world. "The mountain of things I felt I needed to do reached to the moon," writes Bailey, "yet there was little I could do about anything…" But the absence of *doing* allowed her to learn from the slow and immediate world of her snail companion. In fact, she speaks of the snail as her "true mentor" because "it always lived in the moment and was an example of how life, on even the smallest of scales, could be rewarding."

Bailey interweaves her sick-time meditations with numerous facts about gastropods, gleaned from extensive reading long after her condition had improved and her illness stabilized. We learn, for example, that in the world of snails, slime is king. "Slime is the sticky essence of a gastropod's soul, the medium for everything in its life: locomotion, defense, healing, courting, mating, and egg protection." The creatures have many different recipes for slime, each one produced when needed for a specific purpose. Pedal mucus covers the snail's stomach-foot, attaching it tightly to any surface, while minute ripples of muscle allow the snail to move forward. One scientist demonstrated the strength of this mucus attachment by showing that a snail can safely move upside-down across a ceiling burdened with nine times its own weight in reels of cotton.

Other remarkable facts: snails may have thousands of tiny teeth, they love to eat mushrooms, and they are "by no means lacking in intelligence." Snail sex is a very sensuous affair, complicated— though only in human eyes—by the fact that these animals are hermaphrodites, able to assume either the male or female role in any given sexual encounter. The courtship begins when two snails cozy up to one another and wave and touch their tentacles as if smooching. As the affair develops, each shoots a tiny calcium carbonate love dart (literally) into the other. Their bodies press tightly together. Eventually, one of them lays fertilized eggs, although an interval of months may pass before doing so.

This must have happened to Bailey's snail, who one day produced a cluster of eggs. When they hatched, she was able to observe dozens of the snail's miniature offspring develop and thrive. Meanwhile, Bailey's condition gradually improved. She moved back to her own home. Friends released most of the snails into the woods. Finally, when she was able to walk in the woods herself, Bailey set free the last remaining juvenile. Having just crossed her own threshold of release, Bailey reflects, "For the first time, the young snail was in a world without boundaries. I wondered what it would think of this unexpected freedom... How would it choose a territory in this endless wilderness?"

This splendid book gives a glimpse of the deep interrelatedness of living beings, an experience open to any reader who slows down, looks around, and pays close enough attention. ஃ

Jack Coulehan is a poet and physician who teaches at Stony Brook University. His fifth collection of poems, *Bursting With Danger and Music*, will appear in 2011.

Contributors' Notes

Jennifer Barber is the author of the forthcoming *Given Away,* and of *Rigging the Wind* (both from Kore Press). She is the recipient of a Pushcart Prize and the Anna Davidson Rosenberg Award. She edits the literary journal *Salamander* at Suffolk University in Boston, where she teaches literature and creative writing.

Laurel Bastian is the Halls Emerging Artist Fellow at the Wisconsin Institute for Creative Writing. She runs the Writers in Prisons Project in Madison, Wisconsin, and has work in or forthcoming from *Drunken Boat, Puerto del Sol, Anderbo,* and *Margie.*

Beverley Bie Brahic lives in Paris and Stanford, California. A poet and translator, her poems have appeared in *Poetry,* the *Times Literary Supplement,* the *Southern Review,* and *Against Gravity.* Her most recent translations are *Hyperdream* (Hélène Cixous)*; Unfinished Ode to Mud* (Francis Ponge), which was a finalist for the Popescu Prize for Poetry in Translation; and *This Incredible Need to Believe* (Julia Kristeva),which was a finalist for the 2010 French American Foundation Translation Prize.

Jill Caputo was born and raised in Wichita, Kansas. She was a lover of the arts, from indie films to opera, and studied English literature, theatre, and creative writing. She completed an MFA, taught English at Florida State University, and volunteered at the *Southeast Review.* She worked for the Agency of Workforce Innovation, aiding people needing unemployment benefits, while also writing her first novel. She passed away in August 2010, at the age of 30.

Nancy Naomi Carlson is a prize-winning author of two chapbooks and one collection of poetry. She is an associate editor for Tupelo Press and an instructor at the Bethesda Writer's Center. Her work has appeared or is forthcoming in *Agni,* the *Georgia*

Review, Poetry, and the *Southern Review. Stone Lyre,* her translations of the French poet René Char, was just released by Tupelo Press. She holds PhDs in foreign language methodology and school counseling.

Jennifer Chapis has published in magazines and anthologies such as *Arts & Letters, Best New Poets, Colorado Review,* the *Iowa Review,* and *Verse*. She was awarded the Rumi Prize in Poetry chosen by Mark Doty and the Backwards City Poetry Series Prize for her chapbook, *The Beekeeper's Departure*. She is the co-founder of Nightboat Books, and teaches at New York University. Jennifer lives in Brooklyn with her husband, fiction writer Josh Goldfaden.

Elizabeth Crowell has an MFA in creative writing from Columbia University. Her poetry has been published in *Paterson Literary Review, English Journal,* and *Harpur's Palate*. She has taught at the high school and college levels. She is currently the interim English department head at Lexington High School, outside Boston.

Pat Daneman writes poetry and short fiction. She has recently published in *Off the Coast, qarrtsiluni, Blood Orange Review, Cortland Review,* and *Fresh Water*. She has an MA in creative writing from Binghamton University. She lives in Kansas City.

Nicolas Destino is a Buffalo native currently residing in Jersey City. His work has appeared in the *American Poetry Journal, Requited, Broadsided Press, Pitkin Review, Barge Journal,* and as a collection in *Of Kingdoms & Kangaroo* (First Intensity Press). He holds an MFA in creative writing from Goddard College.

Jehanne Dubrow is the author of three poetry collections, most recently *Stateside* (Northwestern University Press). Her work has appeared in *Poetry, New England Review,* the *New Republic, Prairie Schooner,* and *Ploughshares*. She is an assistant professor in literature and creative writing at Washington College.

Danielle Eigner is a family physician in California. As an Air Force physician, she was a flight surgeon in Korea, served at an Italian NATO base, and was deployed to Qatar during the Iraq War. She currently works with immigrants and the underserved. She has an interest in humanitarian aid, and when possible she volunteers abroad. Her story "Condensed Milk" was inspired by her experience as an aid worker in Haiti after the earthquake and during the World Cup.

B.G. Firmani lives in New York City, where she works as a proposal writer for an architecture firm and writes a blog about Italian-American literature, *Forte e Gentile*. She has published fiction in *BOMB* and the *Kenyon Review*. She is a graduate of Barnard College and Brown University, and is currently seeking a publisher for her collection of short stories, *Five Angry Women*.

Gaynell Gavin has published essays in the journals *Fourth Genre*, *Legal Studies Forum*, and *North Dakota Quarterly*. Her work has also been included in the anthologies *Risk, Courage, and Women* (University of North Texas Press) and *The Best of the Bellevue Literary Review* (Bellevue Literary Press). "What We Have," published in *Prairie Schooner*, was included among the "Notable Essays" in *The Best American Essays 2009*. She is a faculty member at Claflin University.

Steve Gehrke has published three books, most recently *Michelangelo's Seizure*, which was selected for the National Poetry Series and published by University of Illinois Press. His other awards include an NEA grant and a Pushcart Prize. He teaches at the University of Nevada-Reno.

Laura Goldin is a publishing lawyer in New York. Her poems have appeared in the *Spoon River Poetry Review* and the *Comstock Review*, among other places.

Kate Lynn Hibbard won the 2004 Gerald Cable Book Award, and her poetry collection *Sleeping Upside Down* was published by Silverfish Review Press in 2006. She teaches writing and women's studies at Minneapolis Community and Technical College. The italicized lines in "Uses for Salt" are quoted from "Women as Workers, Women as Civilizers: True Womanhood in the American West" by Elizabeth Jameson (*Frontiers,* 1984, vol. 7 no. 3).

Patti Horvath's work has appeared in *Shenandoah*, the *Cream City Review*, and *Puerto del Sol*. She is the recipient of a New York Foundation for the Arts Literature Fellowship and is an editor at the *Massachusetts Review*. She teaches at Hofstra University.

Janet Tracy Landman is a semi-retired academic psychologist. Her poetry has appeared in numerous literary journals, including the *Dickinson Review, Icarus, North American Review, Salmagundi*, and *Washington Square*. Her poem "Blue Fire" was awarded first prize in the 2002 National Writers Union competition, judged by Adrienne Rich. Landman is also author of two nonfiction books, *Regret: The Persistence of the Possible* (Oxford) and *Biography of a Conscience: Confessions of Longtime Fugitive Katherine Ann Power* (currently under review).

Jennifer Lee is a graduate of the Johns Hopkins MA Writing Program. Her work has appeared in *JMWW, Brink Magazine*, and the *Potomac Review*. She lives in Baltimore, Maryland.

Joan Leegant is the author of a story collection, *An Hour in Paradise*, which won the PEN/New England Book Award and the Wallant Award for Jewish Fiction, and a novel, *Wherever You Go*, both published by W.W. Norton. Formerly an attorney, since 2007 she has spent half the year in Tel Aviv as the visiting writer at Bar-Ilan University. When not in Israel, she makes her home in Newton, Massachusetts.

Nicholas Patrick Martin grew up in Seattle, Washington. After college, he moved to Cairo, Egypt, where he started writing his first bad novel. He wrote another bad novel, and then a good one— *Zona*—from which the story "Odd a Sea's Wake" is excerpted. He is currently seeking a publisher for *Zona*.

Ben Miller's writing has appeared in the *Kenyon Review, AGNI, Alaska Quarterly Review, Ecotone, Raritan, One Story,* the *Antioch Review* and *Best American Essays*. He has received a creative writing fellowship from the National Endowment for the Arts and the Bright Lights Big Verse award given by the Poetry Society of America.

Brian David Mooney's poems, essays, and short stories have appeared in many literary magazines. He is the recipient of a creation grant from The Vermont Arts Council and National Endowment for the Arts. He is also the creator of The Storymatic, a storytelling game and teaching tool.

Travis Mossotti is an English Lecturer at the University of California, Santa Cruz, and his poetry continues to appear widely. His poem "Decampment" (published in the winter 2010 issue of *Southern Humanities Review*) has recently been adapted to screen as an animated short film (www.decampment.com).

Cynthia Neely's poems have appeared or are forthcoming in *Prime Number, Floating Bridge Review, Raven Chronicles, Quiddity, San Pedro River Review, Autumn Sky, Loch Raven Review,* and *New Millennium Writings*. Her work was included in the anthologies *Poetry for the Mind's Joy*, compiled by Kay Ryan, (US Library of Congress) and *Filled with Breath* (EXOT Books). The natural world, and her place in it, has always been an important subject in her work.

Stacy Nigliazzo is an ER nurse and a lifelong poet. Her work has been featured in *JAMA, AJN,* the *Annals of Internal Medicine* and *The Healing Muse*, in addition to other publications. She is a graduate of Texas A&M University and a recipient of the 2006 Elsevier Award for Nursing Excellence.

Tim Nolan lives in Minneapolis with his wife and three kids and works as a lawyer. His poems have appeared in the *Gettysburg Review,* the *Nation, Ploughshares, Poetry East,* and on the Writer's Almanac. His first book of poems, *The Sound of It,* was published by New Rivers Press in 2008 and was a finalist for the Minnesota Book Award.

Katherine Durham Oldmixon's poems have recently appeared in *Borderlands; Poemeleon; Qarrtsiluni; Big Land, Big Sky, Big Hair: The Best of the Texas Poetry Calendar's First Decade;* and in her chapbook *Water Signs* (Finishing Line). Katherine is Associate Professor of English and Director of the Writing Program at historic Huston-Tillotson University in Austin, Texas. This summer she will teach in Edinburgh, Scotland, in the University of New Orleans's low-residency MFA program.

Benjamin Parzybok is the author of the novel *Couch.* Past projects include *Gumball Poetry*, a literary journal published out of gumball machines; Project Hamad, a campaign to free an innocent Guantanamo inmate from Sudan (now freed!); and The Black Magic Insurance Agency, a one-night game played across the city that blurs reality and fiction. He lives in Portland, Oregon. www.ideacog.net

Emily Sullivan Sanford is a writer and translator living in Berlin. Her recent works of poetry have appeared in *Ditch* and *Chantarelle's Notebook.* Born with achondroplasia, she has been active in disability rights and bioethics from an early age. She is a contributing essayist to the book *Surgically Shaping Children* (Johns Hopkins University Press).

Ruth Schemmel has taught high school English language learners in the Bronx and Washington State, and in Ukraine, through the

U.S. Peace Corps. She lives near Seattle with her husband and two daughters and is at work on a young adult thriller about activism gone awry. "Crazyland" is her first published story.

Gill Schierhout's debut novel, *The Shape of Him*, was nominated for the International IMPAC Dublin Literary Award, and was shortlisted for the Commonwealth Writer's Prize 2010. Her short stories have been published in the United Kingdom, South Africa, and Kenya. She was shortlisted for the Caine Prize for African Writing in 2008. Gill earns a living as an epidemiologist, currently working on a quality-improvement project with indigenous, primary healthcare centers in Australia.

Floyd Skloot's most recent collections of poetry are *The Snow's Music* (LSU Press) and *Selected Poems: 1970-2005* (Tupelo Press), winner of a Pacific NW Book Award and ForeWord Magazine Book of the Year silver award. His seventh collection, *Close Reading*, will be published by Tupelo Press in 2011. Skloot's memoir, *The Wink of the Zenith: The Shaping of a Writer's Life*, was published by the University of Nebraska Press in 2008. He lives in Portland, Oregon.

Virgil Suárez is the author of *90 Miles: Selected and New*, published by the University of Pittsburgh Press. His new book *Indigo* is finished and awaiting publication. When he is not writing, he is busy riding his motorcycles photographing the blue highways of Florida where he lives with his wife and daughters. Mr. Suárez was diagnosed with Hypergraphia Disorder in 1987 and has been making progress ever since.

Anne Valente's fiction appears or is forthcoming in *Hayden's Ferry Review, Unsaid, Annalemma, Hobart*, and Dzanc Books' *Best of the Web 2010* anthology. Her work has been nominated for a 2009 and 2010 Pushcart Prize. Originally from St. Louis, she currently lives and teaches in Ohio.

Acknowledgments

We are deeply grateful to all who have helped support the *Bellevue Literary Review* in its efforts to bridge the worlds of literature and medicine. Special thanks to the Goldenberg family, Marica and Jan Vilcek, and the Burns Archive for their sponsorship of the *BLR* Prizes.

This publication is made possible with public funds from the New York State Council on the Arts, a state agency.

Founder: The Vilcek Foundation

Publisher: The Hassenfeld Foundation

Benefactor: Dr. Arthur Lebowitz

Muses: H. Dale & Elizabeth Hemmerdinger, Dr. William Schaffner, Dr. Joseph Zuckerman

Friends: Dr. Elie M. Abemayor, Dr. Doreen Addrizzo-Harris, Dr. Robert J. Anderson, Dr. Thomas W. Andrews, Dr. Richard J. Baron, Dr. Michael S. Bruno, Dr. Peter Elsbach, Lola Finkelstein, Samuel C. Florman, William Lee Frost, Drs. William & Mary Alice Houghton, Dr. Robin Lifton, Dr. Mark S. Lipton, Dr. Robert Maslansky, Dr. & Mrs. Franco Muggia, Drs. Anthony & Elayne Mustalish, Dr. Richard Nachtigall, Dr. Peter Palese, Eleanor Jackson Piel, Dr. Lionel A. Rudolph, Dr. Rhonda Soricelli, Robert Warshaw, Dr. Michael Yeaman, Dr. Johanna Youner

Supporters: Dr. Jack Ansell, Dr. Charles Debrovner, Dr. Mark Eberle, Dr. Arthur C. Fox, Dr. Robin S. Freedberg, Dr. Frances W. Ginsburg, Dr. Charles S. Hirsch, Dr. Martin L. Kahn, Dr. Sandra Kammerman, Arlene & Richard Kossoff, Dr. Barbara H. Landreth, Dr. Arthur E. Lindner, Dr. Sander H. Mendelson, Dr. Andrew Milano, Dr. Diana Nilsen, Dr. Ira C. Schulman, Dr. Emilia Sedlis, Drs. William & Veronica Slater, Armgard von Bardeleben & Gilbert Tauber, Hans Wyss

We are also grateful to the following subscribers for their support: Peter Acker, Dr. Victor Bressler & Anne Ronne, Felice Buckvar, Ellen L. Case, Dr. Alan R. Fried, Dr. Norman Gevirtz, Elizabeth Ann Lisa, Dr. Joseph I. Mann, Richard E. Rust, Drs. Alan & Constance Tice, Dr. Mary E. Wilson

----

We welcome your support as we continue to explore the connections between literature and medicine. All patrons will be recognized in the journal.

$75 (Supporter), $150 (Friend), and $250 (Muse) – *each includes one-year subscription for you and a friend*
$500 (Benefactor) and $1000 (Publisher) – *each includes three-year subscription for you and a friend*
$5000 (Scribe) and $10,000 (Founder) – *each includes lifetime subscription*

The *Bellevue Literary Review* is part of NYU Langone Medical Center, a 501(c)(3) charitable organization. All contributions are tax-deductible. Please make checks payable to NYU Langone Medical Center - *BLR*.

Bellevue Literary Review, Department of Medicine, NYU Langone Medical Center
550 First Avenue, OBV-A612, New York, NY 10016
www.BLReview.org

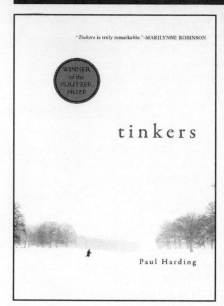
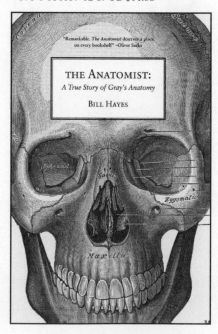

NEW TITLES

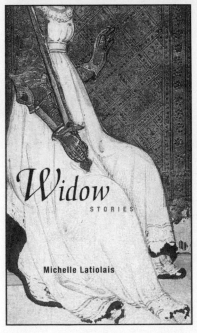

Widow: Stories by **Michelle Latiolais**

"A master of banter, Latiolais is happily bawdy and gorgeously sensual. She is also archly imaginative and psychologically astute..." —*Booklist*

"Sublime . . . [Latiolais] manages to find something luminous in the broken shards—still sharp, still drawing blood—that remain in the wake of losing what could not feasibly be lost." —*The San Francisco Chronicle*

"Latiolais is as close to Alice Munro as a writer can get." —*The Los Angeles Times*

"Michelle Latiolais has given us the rarest item, a splendidly articulated masterpiece." —WILLIAM KITTREDGE, author of *Hole in the Sky* and *The Nature of Generosity*

978-1-934137-30-7 / PB $14.95

The Sojourn by **Andrew Krivak**

"Intimate and keenly observed, *The Sojourn* is a war story, love story, and coming of age novel all rolled into one. I thought of Lermontov and Stendhal, Joseph Roth and Cormac McCarthy as I read. But make no mistake. Krivak's voice and sense of drama are entirely his own." —Sebastian Smee of *The Boston Globe*

"Krivak's sentences accrue and swell and ultimately break over a reader like water: they are that supple and bracing and shining." —Leah Hager Cohen, author of *House Lights*

978-1-934137-34-5 / PB $14.95

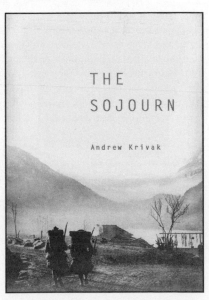

VISIT US ONLINE: www.blpbooks.org

House Arrest
A Novel by Ellen Meeropol
978-1-59709-499-3 / $24.95

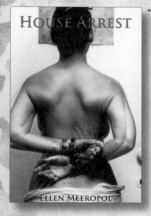

"Meeropol's work is thoughtful and tightly composed, unflinching in taking on challenging subjects and deliberating uneasy ethical conundrums."

—**Publishers Weekly**

In this strong first novel, an unusual relationship develops between a home-care nurse and the pregnant cult member under house arrest to whom she is assigned prenatal visits. Emily Klein suspects that this new assignment has been dumped on her because her boss is trying to get rid of her, but she quickly warms to her new charge, Pippa Glenning, court-ordered to wear an ankle monitor after the deaths by exposure of her 14-month-old daughter and another child in the communal Family of Isis home she lives in—considered a cult by the disapproving community; the two children froze to death during a night of ritualistic celebrations. Emily's ability to empathize with Pippa stems from her own family problems: her father was imprisoned for setting fire to a draft board office during the Vietnam War and Emily provides daily care for her cousin's daughter, born with spina bifida. Throughout, Emily is vexed by the question: is something wrong just because the consequences are awful?

RED HEN PRESS

Available from University of Chicago Distribution Center
To place an order: (800) 621-2736 / www.redhen.org

The Seventh Annual
Bellevue Literary Review Prizes

The *Bellevue Literary Review* Prizes recognize exceptional writing
about health, healing, illness, the mind, and the body.
First prize is $1000 and publication in the Spring 2012 issue
of the *Bellevue Literary Review.*

$1000 Goldenberg Prize for Fiction
Judged by Francine Prose

$1000 Marica and Jan Vilcek Prize for Poetry
Judged by Cornelius Eady

$1000 Burns Archive Prize for Nonfiction
Judged by Susan Orlean

Deadline: July 1, 2011

Submit manuscripts online at www.BLReview.org Prose should be limited
to 5000 words. Poetry submissions should have no more than three poems
(max five pages). Work previously published (including on the Internet)
cannot be considered. Entry fee is $15 per submission. For an additional
$5, you will receive a one-year subscription to the *BLR.*

For complete guidelines,
visit www.BLReview.org

Bellevue Literary Review
Poetry and Prose Reading

Sunday, May 15, 2011, 5pm

Bellevue Hospital Rotunda
462 First Avenue (28th Street) NYC

With readings by:

Patti Horvath
(winner of the Goldenberg Prize for Fiction)
Jennifer Chapis
B.G. Firmani
Ben Miller

Free and open to the public

For more information, please contact us:
info@BLReview.org or 212-263-3973

www.BLReview.org